A HANDBOOK FOR PARENTS IN AND AROUND BATH

First Edition 1990. Second Edition 1993. Third Edition 1997.

Published by Bath With Your Kids, 24 Rockliffe Avenue, Bath BA2 6QP

Printed by Headley Brothers Ltd., Ashford, Kent

Acknowledgments

Many thanks to our dedicated team who have given hours of their time, huge amounts of energy and effort on an entirely voluntary basis. Special thanks go to our families for their endless support, help and encouragement. Thanks also to Marius McKee for setting the adverts, Lesley Sandgrove and Terry Haines for proof-reading, Ann Plant for her typing, Steve Spicer for his invaluable advice (and cups of coffee at all hours). Also the Bath and District branch of the National Childbirth Trust and its members for their support and completion of lots of questionnaires.

We would also like to thank the following organisations: Badgerline, Bath Building Society, Bath Tourist Information Centre, Boggle, Dentons Directory, Hitchcocks, Kimberley Clark, Longleat House, Midland Bank, National Westminster Bank, Praxis, Royal Bank of Scotland, The Golden Cot and Waitrose.

Every effort has been made to ensure that the information in this book is as accurate and up-to-date as possible, but we cannot be held responsible for any consequences that may arise from errors or omissions. While the contents are believed correct at the time of writing, changes may have occurred since that time and will occur during the currency of this book.

Proceeds from the sale of this book will go to the NCT, local children's groups and partly towards financing the next edition. If you would like to help with future editions of Bath With Your Kids, please write to BWYK's, 24 Rockliffe Road, Bathwick BA2 6QP.

© Bath With Your Kids 1997 Illustrations © Jane Gedye 1997
All rights reserved. No part of this publication may be reproduced, stored on a retrieval system or transmitted in any form or by any means without prior permission of the publishers.

ISBN 0 9530178 0 X

Introduction

If you're struggling through town with bags of shopping, a toddler in a pushchair and a reluctant six year old dragging along beside you, when the baby in his front-pack starts wailing for a feed and your two year old suddenly needs the toilet – DON'T PANIC! Just reach for your copy of Bath With Your Kids from your already bulging changing bag and find out where the nearest loo with feeding facilities is located.

In fact, whatever your situation, if you are in Bath with young children, then Bath With Your Kids is an invaluable source of information.

Written by parents for parents, the book includes the essential things you need to know to make life with your kids manageable and hopefully fun too! All the information has been researched by local parents, and much gathered from personal experience.

Bath is a fabulous City, we hope that this book will help you to get the most from it.

Publisher **Paula Haines**

Editor **Elizabeth Spicer**

Research and Section Editors
Denise Blake, Helen Davy, Sue Feldburg, Philippa Forsey, Jane Gedye, Paula Haines, Lynne Locker, Sophie Newman, Sarah Thorn

Production and Artwork **Elizabeth Spicer**

Fund raising and Advertising **Sarah Thorn**

Illustrations by **Jane Gedye** ©1997

City Centre Map supplied by **Dentons Directory** ©

Other Maps © **Bath With Your Kids**

Contents

ADVICE AND SUPPORT	**7**
General Advice and Support	7
Social Security and Money	7
Housing and Heating	8
Social Services	8
Help and Support for Families	8
Help and Support for Women	11
Relationship Problems	11
Ethnic Support Organisations	11
For Children who Need Special Help	12
Help For Parents with a Disability	15
Drug and Alcohol Problems	16
Bereavement	16
ACTIVITIES AND CLUBS	**17**
Creative Activities	17
Art and Craft	17
Dance	17
Drama	18
Music	18
Sports Activities	18
Other Activities	22
After School Clubs	22
Computers	22
Language Clubs	22
Nature and Environment	23
Soft Play Centres	23
Youth Groups	24
Holiday Activities	25
Holiday Sports Courses	26
ANNUAL EVENTS	**27**
BABY AND TODDLER GROUPS	**31**
CHILD CARE	**35**
Childminders and Nannies	35
Babysitters	36

EATING OUT	**37**
City Centre	37
Outside City Centre	43
EDUCATION– PRE-SCHOOL AND PRIMARY	**45**
Day Nurseries and Nursery Schools	45
Playgroups	50
Pre-school Education Voucher System	51
Primary School Admission Policy	52
ENTERTAINMENT AND ENTERTAINERS	**53**
Children's Party Venues in Bath	53
Children's Party Venues Outside Bath	54
Children's Party Entertainers	55
Equipment Hire – Bouncy Castles etc.	57
Theatres	57
Cinemas	58
FUN FOR FREE	**59**
GREEN ISSUES FOR FAMILIES	**61**
Organic Food Supplies	61
Organic Gardening	62
Recycling	62
Reusable Nappies	62
HEALTH CARE	**63**
NHS Family Medicine	63
Health Care for Pregnancy	63
After Your Baby is born	64
Your Child's Health	65
Complementary Medicine	66
Complementary Therapies in Bath	67
LIBRARIES	**69**
Book Libraries	69
Toy Libraries	69
Support Training and Resources	70

Contents

Loo Stops	**71**

Mail Order — 73
Pregnancy Needs	73
Baby and Nursery Equipment	74
Natural Bedding/Green products	75
Children's Fashion – Shoes	76
Children's Fashion – Clothes	76
Books and CD ROM	77
Toys and Gifts	78
Outdoor Play Equipment	79
Party Items and Stocking Fillers	80

Parks and Play Areas — 81
Park Events	81
Parks and Play Areas in Detail	82

Places of Worship — 87

Pubs — 91
Pubs in Bath	91
Pubs Outside Bath	92

Safety — 95

Sanctuaries for Adults — 97
Post Natal Exercise Classes	97
Fitness	97
Adult Education	98
Other	98
Recreation	98

Shops — 99
Baby Equipment	99
Book Shops	99
Charity Shops	100
Clothes – Children and Maternity	100
Hobby Shops	102
Markets	102
Music Shops	103
Party Items and Cakes	103
Shoe Shops	103
Sports, Bike and Dancewear Shops	104
Toy Shops	105
Worth Knowing About	106
Further Afield	108

Swimming Pools and Sports Centres — 109

Trips at a Glance — 112
Trips and Jaunts — 113
Trips and Jaunts in Bath	113
Open Top Bus Tours	116
Guided Walks	116
Trips Afloat – Boat Hire	116
Trips Afloat – Boat Trips	117
Trips and Jaunts Outside Bath	117
Bristol	123
Further Afield	125
Other Sources of Information	126

Walks — 127

Maps — 136-141

Park and Ride — 137

Index — 142

Advice and Support

This chapter lists some of the organisations that can give help and support with the stresses and problems of being a parent - many of these services are free.

Money and housing difficulties can be a crisis point for many families so we include places that can offer help in these areas too.

Some of these organisations are staffed by voluntary, unpaid workers so please do persist in your enquiry if you get an answerphone message or engaged tone when you first call.

GENERAL ADVICE AND SUPPORT

Avon Parents Network

☎ 0117 941 3999 Monday-Friday, 11am-3pm Free information – anything to do with children. Aims to give a fast, accurate and friendly service and will put you in touch with support groups as appropriate.

Bath Centre For Voluntary Service

✉ 3 Abbey Green
☎ 464015
Monday-Thursday 9.30am-12.30/1.30-4.30pm
Information on volunteer groups in Bath. Free resources and a volunteer bureau. Directory of voluntary organisations and community groups 'Directions' for reference or purchase at £5.

Bath Citizens Advice Bureau (CAB)

✉ Edgar Buildings, George Street
☎ 463333/481667
Free confidential and impartial advice. Open to all. Help with benefits, debt, housing, employment, tax, family problems and more. Full debt counselling and benefits service.

Victim Support - Bath District

✉ 12a Westgate Street ☎ 444212
Volunteer-run service which offers counselling and practical help to victims of a crime: help with insurance claims, injury compensation, the security of your property etc.

SOCIAL SECURITY AND MONEY

The Social Security System is complicated, so check what you are entitled to with the DSS or the CAB (see *General Advice*).

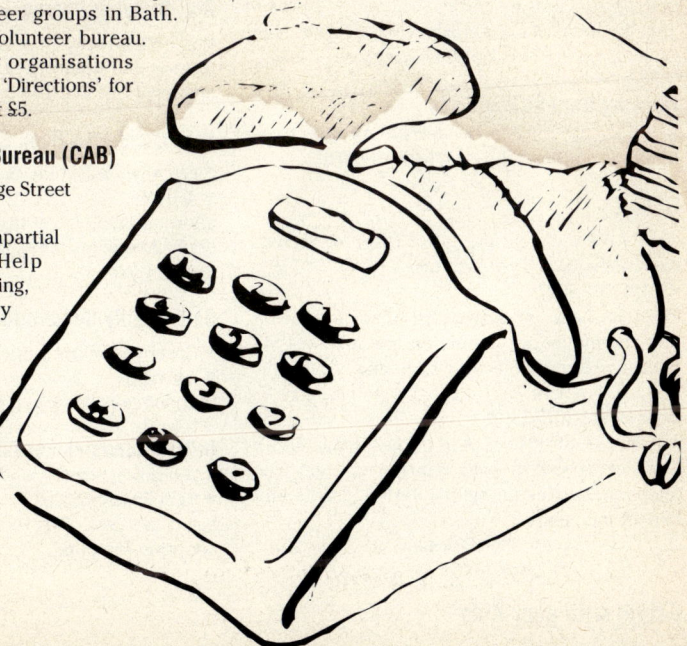

Advice and Support

Social Security
☎ Freeline 0800 666555 (8.30am-4.30pm weekdays)

Family Credit
☎ Helpline 01253 500050 (7.30am -6.30pm weekdays)

Central Bath Office
✉ Kingsmead House, James Street West
☎ 320400

HOUSING AND HEATING

Bath Housing Advice Centre
✉ 18 Kingsmead Square
☎ 448681
Call in or telephone for information or advice on housing matters, everything from finding a new home to tenants rights, debt counselling for mortgage arrears etc. Eviction helpline out of office hours ☎ 336275.

Bath and North East Somerset Council Housing Enquiries
☎ 477000
☎ 477990 (Emergency Housing Maintenance out of hours only)
Specific enquiries are dealt with by area - see Council's entry in telephone directory

Housing Benefit Enquiries
See BANES listing in the telephone directory, different numbers for each area of Bath.

NEA
✉ St Andrew's House, 90/2 Pilgrim Street, Newcastle-upon-Tyne NE1 6SG
☎ 0191 261 5677
Practical help and advice on home insulation and energy use for people on low incomes via the Home Energy Efficiency Scheme.

Winter Warmth Line
☎ 0800 289 404 (Monday to Friday 10am - 4pm) Families at risk in cold weather can get free telephone advice on eg. insulation, grants and benefit payments.
Call Freephone ☎ 0800 289 404

SOCIAL SERVICES

BANES Social Services Department
✉ Lewis House, Manvers Street
☎ 477000
Out of hours emergency number
☎ 01454 615165
- Register of childminders, nurseries, play-groups and playschemes for children under three (they can provide you with a list).
- Services for parents having difficulties in caring for their children.
- Family Support Workers who give practical help in your own home
- Social Services Day Nurseries
- Help with child care fees
- Special needs schemes
- Family Centres, counselling and support
* Foster and residential homes.

HELP AND SUPPORT FOR FAMILIES

Advisory Centre For Education (ACE)
✉ 1b Aberdeen Studios,
22 Highbury Grove, London N5 2DQ
Useful advice for parents of children who experience learning difficulties at school.

Anti-Bullying Campaign
☎ 0171 378 1446
Advice line open 9.30am-5pm Monday-Friday, answerphone at other times.

Bath Children's Book Group
✉ c/o Allyson Jordon, Bath Central Library
☎ 480110
Information on latest titles, newsletter, Carousel books magazine, meetings and events. £6 annual membership.

Bath Family Conciliation Service
✉ Gascoyne House, Upper Borough Walls
☎ 446105
Help for separating and divorcing couples.

British Agencies For Adoption and Fostering
✉ 200 Union Street, London SE1 OLX
☎ 0171 593 2000
Send A5 SAE for list of publications on adoption/fostering.

8 Bath with your Kids

Advice and Support

Child and Family Therapy Service
✉ RU Hospital and 3 North Parade Buildings
☎ 448373
Help and guidance if you are worried by the behaviour of any family member.

Childline
☎ 0800 1111
Call free, 24 hours a day, if you or a child you know is in need of help and advice.

Child Poverty Action Group
✉ 1-5 Bath Street, London EC1V 9PY
☎ 0171 253 3406
A pressure group which represents the interests of low income families.

CRY-SIS
✉ London WC1N 3XX ☎ 0171 404 5011
Emotional and practical support for parents of babies who cry excessively.

The Daycare Trust
✉ 4 Wild Court, London WC2B 4AU
☎ Helpline 0171 405 5167
Fact sheets on finding child care, interviewing carers etc.

End Physical Punishment of Children (EPOCH)
✉ 77 Holloway Road, London N7 8JZ
☎ 0171 700 0627
Send a large SAE for the No Smacking Guide and other guidelines on positive parenting.

Exploring Parenthood
☎ 0171 221 6681
National parenting research centre. Free one-hour phone consultation with a family advisor.

Families Need Fathers
☎ 0171 613 5060
Advice and support on non-custodial fathers' rights, local groups.

Family Caring Trust
✉ 44 Rathfriland Road, Newry, Co.Down BT34 1LD ☎ 01693 64174
Parenting courses and supporting videos. Ask your health visitor what is available locally or contact organisation direct to set up your own group.

Family Mediators Association
☎ 465851(answerphone)
Provides a mediation service for couples who have decided to separate or divorce.

Family Placement Team (Bath and Wansdyke)
✉ Avon Social Services, 180 Frome Road, Combe Down, Bath BA2 5RF ☎ 835600
Information and help with foster parenting. Also deal with applications from prospective adopters and arrange placement of children for adoption.

Gingerbread - Association For One Parent Families
☎ 0117 929 1705
Self-help organisation: advice, information, support, plus social activities.

Kids' Club Network
✉ Bellerive House, 3 Muirfield Crescent, London E14 9SZ ☎ 0171 512 2100
Advice and support on finding or starting an after-school kids club, as well as training for parents and careworkers.

Kidscape
✉ 152 Buckingham Palace Road, London SW1W 9TR
Charity that works to prevent the abuse of children - send SAE for free leaflet "Protect Children From Paedophiles!"

Multiple Births Foundation
✉ Queen Charlotte's and Chelsea Hospital Goldhawk Road, London W6 OXG ☎ 0181 740 3519
Professional support for families with multiple births.

National Childbirth Trust (NCT)
✉ London Head Office, Alexandra House, Oldham Terrace, Acton, London W3 6NH
☎ 0181 992 8637 ☎ Local Enquiries 852362
Offers parents of young children a social support network throughout Bath. Charity staffed by local volunteer mothers. Produces helpful publications on parenthood, national Experiences Register held, can put you in touch with other parents who may have shared your situation.

Advice and Support

National Childminding Association
✉ 8 Masons Hill, Bromley, Kent BR2 9EY
Send A5 SAE for information pack on finding and interviewing a childminder.

National Council For One Parent Families
☎ 0171 267 1361

National Foster Care Association
✉ Leonard House, 5-7 Marshalsea Road, London SE1 1EP
☎ 0171 828 6266

National Stepfamily Association
✉ Chapel House, 18 Hatton Place, London EC1N 8RU ☎ Helpline 0990 168388

New Ways To Work
✉ 309 Upper Street, London N1 2TY
☎ 0171 226 4026 (Monday-Wednesday 12-3pm)
Pressure group who campaign for improved parental rights at work and for more family-friendly working conditions.

NORCAP (National Organisation For the Counselling of Adoptees and Parents)
✉ 112 Church Road, Wheatley, Oxon. OX33 1LU
☎ 01865 875000
Send SAE for information pack on link register for tracing birth families plus counselling services.

NSPCC
☎ Child Protection free Helpline 0800 800 500
☎ Childrens Services Office 01225 791777
Telephone crisis lines for parents who fear they may harm their children or anyone concerned about a child's safety. 24 hour, all year - call any time. All calls treated in confidence.

Parentline
☎ 01702 559900
A confidential help and advice service on any aspect of parenting for parents or carers.

Parent Link
☎ Local contact Safiyyah Cooper 0117 951 4135
☎ Local branch 0171 485 8535
Courses run by parents for parents to improve the quality of their relationships with their children.

Parent Network
✉ 44/6 Caversham Road, London NW5 2DS
☎ 0171 485 8535
A "listening ear" for parents handling the daily ups and downs of family life.

Parents At Work
✉ 45 Beech Street, London EC2Y 8AD
☎ 0171 628 3578
Campaigning organisation aims to persuade employers to adopt family-friendly attitudes. Information on child care, useful Working Parents Handbook, updated annually.

Parent To Parent Information on Adoption Services (PPIAS)
✉ Lower Boddington, Daventry, Northants. NN11 6YB
☎ 01327 260295
National self-help service for prospective adopters and adoptive families.

Single Parents Action Network (SPAN)
☎ 0117 951 4231
A national network of self-help groups.

Single Parents Support Group
☎ Pippa Jenkins 448945
One to one telephone counselling for lone parents plus practical advice.

Single Parent Travel Club
✉ 37, Sunningdale Park, Queen Victoria Road, New Tupton, Chesterfield S42 6DZ
Opportunities for single parents to share low-cost holidays, weekend breaks or share travel costs.

Soldiers, Sailors and Airmans Families Association and Forces Help Society
☎ 483538
Practical help and advice for services families.

Twins and Multiple Births Association (TAMBA)
✉ PO Box 30, Little Sutton, South Wirral, L66 1TH
☎ 0151 348 0020
☎ Helpline 01732 868000 (7-11pm, weekends 10am-11pm)
Advice and support for parents and expectant

Advice and Support

parents of multiple births. Information pack, books and leaflets. Specialist support groups eg. Supertwins for those with triplets or more, bereavement support etc. Will give details of local groups or send club starter pack.

HELP AND SUPPORT FOR WOMEN

Association For Postnatal Illness
✉ 25 Jerdan Place, Fulham, London SW6 1BE
☎ 0171 386 0868
One to one support for mothers.

Avon Sexual Abuse Centre
✉ PO Box 665, Bristol BS99 1XY ☎ 0117 935 1707
Telephone counselling and individual advice sessions offered in Bristol.

Bath Domestic Violence Forum
☎ Adviceline 464602

Bath Women's Aid
☎ 466989
Advice, support and refuge for women and children suffering domestic violence. Contact via Social Services Dept. or police.

Bristol Crisis Centre For Women
✉ PO Box 654, Bristol BS99 1XH ☎ 0117 925 1119
Confidential helpline for women throughout South West who are in emotional distress. Self-help groups, plus training workshops, talks and seminars.

Meet A Mum Association (MAMA)
✉ 14 Willis Road, Croydon Surrey CR0 2XX
☎ 0181 665 0357
Moral support and practical help for women suffering post-natal depression or feeling isolated or lonely after the birth of a child. Details of West Country groups on request.

National Endometriosis Society
☎ 0171 222 2776

National Women's Register
☎ Penny Lorenc 314923
Offers women with enquiring minds chance to meet in each others' homes for stimulating, wide-ranging discussions on many subjects.

Women's Aid Helpline
☎ 0117 963 3542

Women's Legal Advice Line
✉ 35 Brock Street, Bath BA1 2LN
☎ 423703 (Monday-Friday 9am-5pm)
Free, confidential legal advice for women by women solicitors.

Women Returners Network
✉ 100 Park Village East, London NW1 3SR
☎ 0171 468 2290
Help, support, training and confidence-boosting for those planning to re-enter the world of work after a child care break.

RELATIONSHIP PROBLEMS

Brook Advisory Service
✉ 25 Denmark Street, Bristol BS1 5DQ
☎ 0117 929 0090
Counselling/advice on sexual problems and contraception and emergency contraception etc. Daytime appointments, general advice and free walk-in sessions.

RELATE
(formerly Marriage Guidance Council)
✉ 21 Milsom Street, Bath
☎ 465593
Counselling service for people experiencing difficulties in their relationship and sex therapy for people in committed relationships. Appointments necessary.

ETHNIC SUPPORT ORGANISATIONS

Association of Jamaicans
✉ 67 Ringswell Gardens, Bath BA1 6BN
Group that promotes the social, cultural and economic interests of Jamaicans living in the UK.

Avon Chinese Association
✉ 4-5 King Square, Bristol BS2 8JG
☎ 0117 924 0797
Recreational and cultural facilities for Chinese families.

Advice and Support

Bangladesh Association
✉ 9 Barrow Road, Odd Down ☎ 840028
Tuition in the mother tongue for Bangladeshi children, a meeting point for women and support for disabled Bangladeshis.

Bath Asian Council
✉ 27a Westgate Street Bath BA1 1EP ☎ 332231
Counselling service offering help with social, relationship, addiction, employment and immigration problems. Promotes a better understanding of Asian people and their culture in and around Bath. Social functions organised. Language classes in Hindi, Urdu and Punjabi according to demand and availability of volunteer tutors.

Bath Black and Other Minority Ethnic Network
✉ 3 Abbey Green, Bath BA1 1NW ☎ 333703
An umbrella organisation giving developmental support to the black voluntary sector in Bath. Identifies training and resource needs, collates and publicises useful information.

Bath Black Parents and Governors Support Group
✉ c/o Bath Racial Equality Council, First Floor, 24 Westgate Street BA1 1EP
☎ 442352
Parents of black and other minority ethnic children working to foster an environment where children receive an education that gives them greater self confidence, a sense of pride in their identity and history and the opportunity to gain equal access to further and higher education and employment.

Bath West Indian Social Activity Centre (BWISAC)
✉ 3 Long Acre, London Road ☎ 461636
Busy social centre with lots of family-friendly activities - café, information service, play opportunities etc.

Chinese Women's Group
✉ St Agnes Parish Church, Thomas Street, St Paul's, Bristol BS2 9LL
☎ 0117 935 1462
Support for those who may feel isolated and far from their family eg. after having a child.

Multi Racial Club
✉ Percy Community Centre, Percy House, New King Street, Bath ☎ C.Cowan 317099
Meet Saturday 10am-12 noon.
For anyone interested in fostering good relations between racial groups. Families especially welcome.

STAR
(Support and Training Against Racism)
✉ 7 Barton Buildings, Bath BA1 2JR
☎ 334415
Works for racial equality in the education of under-fives. Training and multi-cultural resource materials available on loan.

Travellers Support Group
✉ c/o Shelter, Bristol BS1 3HX ☎ 0117 926 8115 (messages will be passed on)
Campaigns for site provision and works to prevent eviction, particularly where families have special healthcare needs.

FOR CHILDREN WHO NEED SPECIAL HELP

Action For Sick Children (NAWCH Ltd.)
✉ 32 Combe Park BA1 3NR
☎ P Reeves 421480
Advice and support for parents and carers of sick children.

Aled Richards Trust (Bath)
✉ 1/2 Bridewell Lane ☎ 444347
Information and support for people infected and affected by HIV and AIDS. Buddying, counselling, complementary therapies, groups, small grants and drop-in. Home visits.

Association For Children With Life-Threatening Conditions (ACT)
✉ 65 St Michaels Hill, Bristol ☎ 0117 922 1556

Avon Autistic Foundation
☎ 0117 982 3229

National Autistic Society
✉ 276 Willesden Lane, London NW2 5RB
☎ 0181 451 1114
☎ Helpline 0181 830 0999 (10am - 3pm weekdays)

Advice and Support

Bath Mencap Society
☎ 0117 986 0437
Friendship, encouragement and help for families with a mentally handicapped child or adult.

Bath Mencap and Gateway Sports Club
Bath Sports Centre, North Parade Road
☎ Brian Downes 742265
☎ Sam Evans 332397
☎ Alison Francis 864872
Thursdays, dry-sports 6-7pm, swimming 7-8pm. For people with a mental handicap and families. Low fees, free entry for accompanying adults. Followed by social session with créche provided. Other social outings.

Bath Opportunity Group
✉ Rosemary Lodge, Upper Wellsway (below St. Martin's Hospital)
☎ 835669
Playgroup for children with physical or mental difficulties or other special needs, and their siblings 0-5 years. Free transport can be arranged. Also Mums Support Group on 2nd Thursday every month (except school holidays).

Rescue Foundation For the Brain Injured Infant
✉ Kingsgate House, Church Road, Kingswood
☎ 0117 940 1111

Bristol Royal Society For The Blind
✉ Stillhouse Lane, Bedminster BS3 4EB
☎ 0117 953 7750 (voice and minicom)
BRSB has an extensive range of equipment (including games) for children with a visual impairment. Information on local services.

Cancer & Leukaemia in Childhood Trust (CLIC)
✉ 12 King Square, Bristol
☎ 0117 924 8844

Children's Liver Disease Foundation
☎ 0121 643 7182

Cleft Lip and Palate Association (CLAPA)
✉ 134 Buckingham Palace Road, London SW1W 9SA

Contact A Family
✉ 170 Tottenham Court Road, London W1P OHA
☎ 0171 383 3555
Links families who have children with disabilities or special needs via self-help groups.

Cystic Fibrosis Comfort Fund
✉ PO Box 32, Bristol BS99 1PT
☎ 0117 949 6603
Has books and information. Will try to provide funds for special equipment or other expenses according to a family's needs.

Cystic Fibrosis Research Trust
✉ 2 Broadoak Cottage, Wells Road, Dundry BS18 8NE ☎ Anne Reece 0117 978 3175
Information services and meetings plus a network of volunteer family supporters.

Cystic Fibrosis Trust
✉ Alexandra House, 5 Blyth Road, Bromley, Kent BR1 3RS ☎ 0181 464 7211

Royal National Institute for Deaf People
✉ 13B Church Farm Business Park, Corston BA2 9AP
☎ 874460 (voice and minicom)
Information, training and interpretation - loop in meeting room.

British Diabetic Association
✉ 10 Queen Anne Street, London W1M OBD
☎ 0171 323 1531
Telephone for information of nearest groups.

Downs Syndrome Association
☎ Claire Turner 0117 951 6214 (Bristol/Bath)
☎ Tony Clark 01934 514510 (North Somerset)

Dyslexia Association
☎ 832691

Dyslexia Institute,
✉ Huntingdon Centre, Vineyards ☎ 420554
Assessment, training, teaching and publications to assist children with learning difficulties.

Dyspraxia Foundation
✉ 8 West Alley, Hitchin, Herts. SG5 1EG
☎ 01462 454986
Information on 'clumsy child syndrome'.

Bath with your Kids 13

Advice and Support

National Eczema Society
✉ 163 Eversholt Street, London NW1 1BU
☎ 0171 388 4097
Advice, information and resources.

British Epilepsy Association
✉ Anstey House, 40 Hanover Square,
Leeds LS3 1BE ☎ 0345 089599
Information pack and local self-help groups.

National Society For Epilepsy
✉ Chalfont St Peter, SL9 ORJ
☎ 01494 873991

ERIC-Eneuresis Resource and Information Centre
✉ 34, Old School House, Brittania Road, Kingswood
Bristol BS15 2DB ☎ 0117 960 3060
Help with bedwetting problems.

Faith and Light
✉ St. Joseph's, Sladebrook Road, Twerton
☎ 318828
Special needs families and friends group. Meet 3rd Monday of month, 7.30-9pm, except August, for worship and activities. Refreshments.

Haemophilia Society
✉ 123 Westminster Bridge Road,
London SE1 7HR ☎ 0171 928 2020
Free advice, information and self-help support.

HEADWAY (National Head Injuries Association)
✉ 7 King Edward Court, King Edward Street,
Nottingham NG1 1EW ☎ 0115 924 0800
Information, advice, care and rehabilitation.

Attention Deficit Hyperactivity Disorder (ADHD) Family Support Group
☎ 01380 726710
Advice on family counselling, educational support and help in changing behaviour.

The Hyperactive Children's Support Group
☎ 01903 725182

The Informed Parent Group
✉ 19 Woodlands Road, Harrow, Middx HA1 2RT
☎ Local contact Chris Wilkinson 0117 963 2306
Inoculation and other child health issues.

Leukaemia Care Society
✉ 14 Kingfisher Court, Exeter EX4 8JN
☎ 01392 464848

Lifetime Service
☎ 420785
Department of Health initiative provides teaching and supporting role for parents and siblings of children with life-threatening and chronic illnesses.

Meningitis Research Foundation
✉ 13 High Street, Thornbury, Bristol BS12 2AE
☎ 01454 413344
Information and 24 hour helpline.

National Meningitis Trust
✉ Fern House, Bath Road, Stroud
Gloucestershire GL5 3TJ
☎ 0345 538118
Leaflets and advice - 24-hour support line.

MIND (Association For Mental Health)
✉ 13 Abbey Churchyard, Bath BA1 1LY
☎ 463525

Motor Neurone Disease Association
✉ PO Box 246, Northampton NN1 2PR
☎ 0345 626262
Information for sufferers and their carers.

North East Somerset Trust For Children
✉ Kelson House, Tilley Lane,
Farmborough BA3 1BE
☎ Jennifer Pearce 01761 470165
Provides financial support for local children who have suffered or are suffering abuse, neglect or poverty. Other services include outings, Christmas party and toys loan service.

Patient Information Publications
✉ 50 The Grove, Gosforth,
Newcastle upon Tyne NE3 1NJ
☎ 0191 285 1874
Well-written, jargon-free leaflets with advice on nearly 200 medical conditions. Database of 250 self-help groups available, access via GP.

The Pituitary Foundation
✉ 17/18 The Courtyard, Woodlands, Almondsbury,
Bristol BS12 4NQ
☎ 01454 201612
Advice and support to patients and families.

Advice and Support

Professional Association of Tutors
✉ 63 King Edward Road,
Northampton NN1 5LY
One to one tuition/extra help with learning. Send SAE and your telephone number for details of tutors in the area.

SCOPE (for people with cerebral palsy)
✉ Pamwell House, 106 Pennywell Road, Easton BS5 OTX
☎ 0117 941 4424
☎ Freephone helpline 0800 626 216
☎ Computers for life: advice on the technology available to assist those with cerebral palsy 01275 891713.
Range of services including care and support for families.

Sickle Cell Society
✉ 54 Station Road, Harlesden, NW10 4UA
☎ 0181 961 7795
Leaflets and info. pack on setting up self-help groups. Welfare and education grants plus free summer holidays for affected children.

Spina Bifida & Hydrocephalus Association
✉ G Egan, 64 Rookery Road, Knowle, Bristol BS4 2DT
☎ 0117 977 7942

STEPS (Specialised Toys Educational Postal Service)
☎ Paul Hames 01803 552012
Volunteer-run charity, adapts battery operated toys to needs of disabled children. Lends them free for three month periods.

Supporting Holidays For Disabled Children
☎ 833406
Local charity which funds breaks for disabled and sick children.

Supportive Parents For Special Children
☎ 0117 977 2225 (helpline)
☎ 0117 977 5289
Help, support, information and social contact. Bath meetings held.

What Doctors Don't Tell You
4 Wallace Road, London N1 2PG
Subscription-only publication which reprints information from medical journals.

Help For Parents With a Disability

Access Bath & North East Somerset
✉ PO Box 1975, Bath BA2 8YB ☎ 448855
Disabled people tackling access issues.

Action For ME (Myalgic Encephalitis)
✉ PO Box 1302, Wells BA5 2WE ☎ 01749 670402 (Counselling) ☎ 0891 122976 (Information)

Bath Community Transport
✉ St Martin's Hospital, Midford Road ☎ 832317
Specially equipped vehicles for anyone in need - advance notice of travel requirements must be given by phone.

Bath and Wansdyke Society For the Blind and Partially Sighted
✉ 7 Green Park Station, Bath BA1 1JB
Resources and meeting room. Befriending service, small grants for travel and services.

Bath Shopmobility Centre
✉ 4 Railway Street (behind Bus Station)
☎ 481744 Minicom/Fax 481773
Low cost loan of wheelchairs and electric scooters. Free copies of the BANES Access Guide to Bath.

Benefit Enquiries For People With Disabilities
☎ 0800 882200 (8.30am-6.30pm weekdays, 9am-1pm Saturdays)
☎ 0800 243355 (Minicom)

Bristol Shopmobility
✉ Unit 26, Castle Gallery, The Galleries Shopping Centre, Broadmead, Bristol BS1 3XE
☎ 0117 922 6342 (see Bath listing above).

British Council of Organisations of Disabled People
✉ Litchurch Plaza, Litchurch Lane, Derby DE24 8AA

Disability Living Allowance Customer Care Helpline
☎ 0345 123456 (weekdays 7.30am-6.30pm)

The Disabled Living Foundation
✉ 380/4, Harrow Road, London W9 2HV
☎ 0171 289 6111
Help and advice on all aspects of daily living.

Bath with your Kids 15

Advice and Support

The Multiple Sclerosis Centre
✉ Unit 41/2 Southfield Trading Estate, Nailsea BS19 1JD ☎ 01275 858806

Multiple Sclerosis Society – Bath & District Branch
✉ Miss G M Huggins (Sec), 24 Warminster Road, Bathampton BA2 6SA ☎ 460047

RADAR (Royal Association For Disability and Rehabilitation)
☎ 0171 250 3222

SWAN Disability Information Service
✉ 5 Wells Hill, Radstock BA3 3RN ☎ 01761 435768
Local and National information service.

Tripscope
☎ 0117 941 4094
Transport information for people with disabilities helps plan travel with confidence.

West Of England Coalition of Disabled People
✉ 6 Somerville Road, Bishopston BS7 9AA
☎ 0117 949 7707

Drug And Alcohol Problems

Alcohol Advisory Centre
✉ First Floor, 16 Milsom Street ☎ 464374

Al-Anon
☎ 317181
Help for families and friends of problem drinker. Monday meetings 8-9pm at Abbey Church House, Bath (side door).

Alcoholics Anonymous
✉ PO Box 42, Bristol BS99 7RW
☎ 0117 926 5520 / 5986
Bath meetings run by people who have experienced drink problems.

Bath Area Drugs Advisory Service
✉ 32/3 Broad Street, Bath ☎ 469379
Open Monday, Tuesday, Thursday, Friday 10.30 am-4.30 pm. Appointments am, drop-in sessions pm, open to all for tea and counselling.

Drinkline
☎ 0345 32 02 02 (low cost call)
Confidential counselling and information.

Narcotics Anonymous
✉ PO Box 285, Bristol BS99 7AS ☎ 0117 924 0084
Recorded message about future meetings.

Turning Point
Broad Street House, 1/5 Broad Street, Wells Somerset BA5 2DJ

Bereavement

The Compassionate Friends
☎ 0117 953 9639
Support for bereaved parents by bereaved parents.

Cruse Bereavement Care
✉ 2 Hetling Court, Bath BA1 1SH ☎ 465878
Counselling, advice, practical information for anyone bereaved. Opportunities for social contact with other bereaved parents.

Foundation For The Study Of Infant Deaths
✉ 14 Halkin Street, London SW1X 7DP
☎ 0171 235 1721 (24 hour cot death helpline)
Cot death research and support - local groups.

Miscarriage Association
✉ c/o Clayton Hospital, Northgate, Wakefield, West Yorks WF1 3JS ☎ 01924 200799 (24 hour)
Information, advice and support for women who have suffered a miscarriage or who fear that they might. Local contacts/groups.

SATFA
✉ 29-30 Soho Square, London W1V 6JB
☎ 0171 439 6124
Support for parents after termination of a pregnancy due to a foetal abnormality.

Stillbirth and Neonatal Death Society (SANDS)
✉ 28 Portland Place, London W1N 4DE
☎ 0171 436 5881
Self-help group run by parents who have experienced a stillbirth or neonatal death. Local support may be available.

16 Bath with your Kids

Activities and Clubs

Creative Activities

Art and Craft
Clay Modelling Fun
✉ Weston Village
☎ Mrs Hodgson 318649
5-week courses for children aged 8 years and over. Wednesday/Thursday 6.30-7.45pm and Saturday 9-10.30am. Also play scheme sessions for children 5 years and over during some school holidays. Must be booked in advance.

The Women's Woodwork Centre
✉ Larkhall
☎ 852633/339482
Safe and fun woodworking classes for 7 years+. Six week course after school or Saturdays – take home a toy, game or simple piece of furniture. Also hold workshops for specific items: collage picture frames, dinosaurs and robots etc.

Young Textiles Group
☎ Alison Harper 466994
Workshop for children from 7 years upwards. Wide variety of creative activities using textiles, including printing, dying, felt-making, stitching, embroidery and knitting.

Dance
Bath Dancecentre
✉ Forum Buildings Ballroom
☎ 461834
Rock-'n-roll, Disco and Latin American dancing for children of any age – tiny tots welcome. Saturday morning classes during term times, payable weekly.

Dorothy Coleburn School of Dancing
✉ Englishcombe Court, Englishcombe Lane
☎ 335087/313036
Daily classes in ballet, tap and jazz dance, for boys and girls aged 3-18 years. Classes for pre-school children held at 2pm on weekdays; all other classes are held after school and all day Saturday. Also adult tap and ballet classes. Uniform dance gear worn. The School provides children for fashion, pantomime, shows and filming work.

Debbie Christine School of Dance
✉ Peasedown St. John ☎ 01761 472109
Ballet, tap and modern dance for 3 years upwards. Exams available.

Karan Lesley Dance
☎ 319164
Ballet, modern and tap classes held in Larkhall, Widcombe and Monmouth Street. Start with 'Mini-ballet' for pre-school children and progress to examination classes. 10 week terms payable in advance. Uniform dance gear worn.

Mum and Me (but Dads/Grandads etc. very welcome!) ☎ 425012
Classes run by Health and Beauty Exercise at St. Mark's Community Centre, Widcombe, Freshford Memorial Hall and Bathford Parish Hall. Movement to live piano music with rhymes, songs, hoops and balls. £1.50 fee then pay weekly for classes. Term times only. Classes for under-3's and 3-4 years+.

Oldfield Dance Centre
✉ Oldfield School ☎ Julia Tuckey 423582
Opportunity to do GCSE Dance. After school.

Scottish Country Dance
✉ Central United Reformed Church Hall, Grove Street ☎ 01275 472634 or 01249 444773
Saturday mornings 9am, 10 week terms, payable half-termly. Boys and girls 7-17 years.

Utopia Baton Twirlers
☎ Sarah Foley 01761 433521
Ages 6-18 years. Monday, Hayesfield School, Oldfield Park; Tuesday, Methodist Church Hall, Oldfield Park, 6.30-8.30pm. Baton twirling dancing, marching, cheerleading, competitions countrywide. Professional trainers. £1.50 per session. Phone for information sheet.

Bath with your Kids

Activities and Clubs

Wendy Clark School of Ballet
☎ 832886
Age 3 ballet and tap, at Widcombe Infant School, every Wednesday at 4pm. For older children up to 16, throughout week at St.Mark's Community Centre, Widcombe. Follow Royal Academy of Dance syllabus. Payable termly.

DRAMA
Loud and Proud
✉ Percy Community Centre, New King Street
☎ 01249 653785
Theatre workshops for 9-12's. Meet weekly, Saturday 11am-12.30. Work towards performance held in June. £2.50 per week. See *Holiday Activities* for other courses.

Merlin Theatre Arts Club
✉ Merlin Theatre, Frome
☎ 01373 465949
Saturdays in term time 10am-12pm. 7-11 years olds. Normally join for one month, different theme each month. Phone for brochure.

The Rondo
✉ Larkhall, Bath ☎ 444003
Occasional children's workshops and holiday courses.

Theatre Royal Youth Theatre
☎ 448815
For ages 7-9 and 9-14 years. Meet weekly, no auditions. Children can be involved in area of theatre that interests them: acting, directing, scenery painting etc. Regular performances held in Ustinov Studio. Also workshops and skills related courses during the holidays.

Weston Theatre Group
☎ 332105
Age 5-15 years. Meets Friday 7-9pm at Parish Hall, Weston (behind Scout Hall opposite Kings Head). Work towards performances involving acting, dancing and singing. Extra rehearsals, Sundays 6-8pm as performances approach. Children can also be involved backstage. Pay 70p weekly.

MUSIC
Bath Hobby Horse Club
☎ 0117 9249894
Singing, playing and folk dancing for children up to 13 years. Meet once a month on a Sunday at 2.30-4.30pm at a venue in Bath.

Bath Philharmonia Youth
☎ 421184
Formed to provide encouragement to young musicians with commitment and talent to play in a symphony orchestra or symphonic wind band. Playing at Grade 7 or beyond. Major performance, three times a year.

Bath Society of Young Musicians
✉ City of Bath College, Beau Street
☎ Carole Timms, Bath and North East Somerset Music Service 395110
Saturday mornings termly. Children of all ages. Senior orchestra, string orchestras, wind bands, recorder groups and choirs. Regular concerts.

Music Makers
✉ St.Matthews Church Hall, Widcombe
☎ Clare Core 333274
For children aged 2-4. Singing, movement to music, instrument and art work. In a fun and relaxed atmosphere. Younger siblings are welcome. Tuesday 9.30-10.15am. During term time only. £2.50 per session, payable half termly.

Opus Music Workshops
☎ 460209
Group workshops aim to encourage gradual development of musical skills. Singing, action songs, musical games and playing percussion instruments. 3 age groups: Under 2's, 2-3 years and 3-4 years. Group Piano Teaching for 5 years plus. Pay termly (trial workshops available).

SPORTS ACTIVITIES

Bath Sports Development
☎ 462366
Sports Development is a small team within the Leisure Services Department of Bath and North East Somerset Council which provides active support to promote and develop sport throughout the area.
They offer a wide range of services including organising after school sports clubs, helping sports clubs, running quality coaching schemes and arranging holiday sports coaching courses.
Phone for more details or to be added to their mailing list.

Activities and Clubs

ATHLETICS
Sports Hall Athletics Fun Club
☎ 462366
Held at Bath Sports and Leisure Centre. Occasional athletics course on Saturday mornings and during holidays. For 8-13's.

City of Bath Athletics
☎ 420927
All year round training. Summer track competitions, winter cross-country and some indoor events. Family members aged 7+, individuals aged 9+.

BADMINTON
Bath Junior Badminton Club
☎ Duncan Light (qualified coach) 866239
Coaching and competitions for 10's+. Bath Sports Centre, Friday 6.30-9.30pm. £2 weekly.

BASKETBALL
KBI Basketball Club
☎ 462563
Based at Bath Sports and Leisure Centre, meet on Sunday afternoons for training. Minis aged 8-12 years, 3.30-4.30pm, Juniors aged 13-16 years, 4.30-5.30pm.

CANOEING
Bath Canoe Club
✉ The Old Organ Factory, Cleveland Cottages
☎ 445549
Wednesday 6.30pm, Sunday 2.30pm during the summer. Under 10's can join as family members only. Children are welcome at training sessions, but must be accompanied by a parent. Pool sessions are held during winter, on Sundays.

CRICKET
Bear Flat Youth Cricket Club
☎ 429146
Membership is open to both boys and girls between 8 and 17 years. Coaching courses in the winter and regular Sunday morning practices in the spring and summer. There is an under-10s team and all members have the opportunity to play in matches. Costs are kept low – the club is non-profit making and run mainly by the parents, many of whom play as well.

Cricket Coaching for Girls
✉ Peter Wight's Cricket School, North Parade
☎ Nicola Tranter 862720
Indoor training sessions Saturday 4-5pm from February to Easter; in summer there are outdoor practices which are held in Corsham, every Thursday 6.15 till dusk, and some matches. Kit is provided. Small fee plus weekly 'nets' fee of 50p.

FOOTBALL
Avon Arsenal Under 13's
☎ Ian Lanning 312328
Football training for 9-13's on Wednesdays, 5.15pm at St.Marks Community School, Baytree Road, Larkhall. Pay weekly.

Football Factory
✉ Sports Hall, Newton Park Campus, Bath College of H.E. ☎ 874238
Sessions throughout year. Saturday 10am-1pm for children 6-10 years. Pay weekly.

The Soccerworks
✉ Held at Beechen Cliff School, Bear Flat
☎ Stewart Naughton 333771
Introduction to football for 5-14 years. Penalty shoot-outs, 5-a-sides, competitions. Saturdays 10am-12.30pm and Sundays 2.30-5pm. Pay as you go, £2.50 plus money for tuck shop at breaktime. Also structured fun activity days during holidays, 9.30am-3.30pm.

GYMNASTICS
Baskerville's Gym Fun
✉ Burnham Road, Lower Bristol Road ☎ 339991
Gym classes for pre-school children, 6 months-2 years: Creepy Crawlies 6-18 months, with parents, Playgym 18months-2 years, with parents. Children's recreational classes (school age). Also Birthday Parties (see **Entertainments**).

Baskerville's
✉ Englishcombe Lane ☎ 330001
Daily gymnastic classes for 2-4 years. Junior and Senior Recreational, Badge and Competition classes, Monday to Saturday during term-time. Book termly, pay in advance. Day and half-day 'fun gym' sessions for 3 years upwards during school holidays - bookable in advance. Also has adult classes with Crèche available.

Activities and Clubs

"ENGLISHCOMBE COURT"
Englishcombe Lane, BATH
01225 330001

FULLY EQUIPPED PURPOSE BUILT FITNESS CENTRE
Aerobics Step Circuit Training Body Toning
EVENING & DAYTIME (crèche available)

Sauna Solarium Weights Room
Coffee Bar Large Car Park

GOLD & FITNESS MEMBERSHIP
available - Excellent Value!

ALL TEACHERS FULLY QUALIFIED

Baskerville's is also the best equipped Gymnastics Centre in the South West
**All ages and abilities catered for –
2 years>Adults
Recreational>National Level Classes**

Burnham Road, Lower Bristol Road, Bath

*A whole range of classes to suit everyone in a relaxed, fun atmosphere
Come along and see us!*

CREEPY CRAWLIES (approx. 6-18 mths)
PLAYGYM (approx. 18 mths-2¼ yrs)
RECREATIONAL GYM BADGE WORK
(B.A.G.A.) (school age children)
CHILDREN'S BIRTHDAY PARTIES (1-9 years)
FITNESS CLASSES (Aerobics & Circuit Training)

**CALL US ON TEL: 01225 339991
FOR FURTHER INFORMATION**

Bath Sports and Leisure Centre
☎ 462563
Gym for 2-3 year olds, Wednesday 9.30-10.30am. Gym and Swim for 2-3s and 3-4s, Wednesday and Thursday, 11.00am-12.30pm. Gym and Jump for 3-4s (with trampolining), Wednesday 1.30-2.30pm.

GymKids, Bath Sports Development
☎ Joy Morton 396431
Mini aged 4-7 and Gymkids aged 7-11. Classes held at Bath Sports and Leisure Centre. Provide a link between school and club gymnastics.

MARTIAL ARTS
Bath Aikido
✉ 42 Chilton Road ☎ 318242
Monday evenings at Hayesfield Lower School: 6.30-8.00pm Juniors 5-15 years, 8.00-10.00pm Seniors. Friday evenings at the Garraway Centre, Larkhall: 6.00-7.00pm Juniors 5-7 years, 7.00-8.00pm Juniors 8-15 years, 8.00-10.00pm Seniors.

Bath Judo Club
☎ 428569
At Garraway Youth Club, Larkhall, Saturday 10am for 7 years+, Monday 6.30pm for 8 years+. Bath Sports Centre, Friday 6pm for 8 years+. Also Wednesday class. Pay termly.

Bath Tae Kwon-do
☎ 0117 9407087
Lessons at Bath Sports Centre on Sunday 6.30-7.30pm and at King Edwards School on Wednesday 6-7pm for age 6+. Pay weekly.

Kickers
✉ Upper Bristol Road ☎ 461463
Karate and Tae Kwan-do from 5 years. Karate Saturday 10-12noon. Payable weekly. Tae Kwan-do. Tuesday and Friday 4.45-6pm. and Saturday 3-5pm. Payable monthly.

RIDING
Wellow Trekking Centre
✉ Little Horsecroft Farm, Wellow ☎ 834376
1/2 hour treks throughout the year (except Christmas). Short walks on leading rein for children 3+. Lessons for 5-6's Saturday and Sunday mornings. Pub Ride, 10.00-2.00pm (includes 1 hour for pub lunch).

20 Bath with your Kids

Activities and Clubs

Roller Skating
Bath Sports and Leisure Centre
☎ 462563
Saturday afternoons. Boot/skate hire, sizes: kid's 10-adult 10. Courses on Tuesday 4.30-5.30pm, mixed ability, any age, 12 weeks. Children should be accompanied by adult.

Rugby (Mini Rugby)
Until 9 years old, children play 'New Image' rugby - a unisex, non-contact form of the game specially designed for young players. They then play 'mini rugby' until 12 years when they play the full game.

Avon Rugby Club
✉ Hicks Field, London Road West, Batheaston
☎ 466637
Membership open to boys and girls 6 years and over. Sunday 10am-12 noon, September-May. Qualified coaches. £20 for the year.

Bath Football Club (RFU)
✉ Bath Recreation Ground ☎ 314455
For boys and girls 6 years and over. Sunday 10.30am-12pm, September-May. £20 for year's membership includes free entry to BFC matches.

Sailing
Bristol Avon Sailing Club
✉ Mead Lane, Saltford ☎ 400127
Family club with racing on Thursdays and Sundays and sailing at other times. No waiting list; any class of boat. Courses for over 10's.

Swimming
Bath Dolphin Swimming Club
☎ 460612
Lessons and training from 5 years. Tuesday 7pm at Bath Sports Centre all year and at Kingswood School, term times on Thursday and Friday. Annual subscription paid in April covers all fees and admissions.

Bath Flippers
☎ 311350/420550
Lessons at Kingswood School. Saturday morning classes, for children from 5 years. 10 week terms, also summer holiday courses.

Bath Sports and Leisure Centre
☎ 462563
Waterbabies/Watertots, age 3 months-1 year/1-2 years: five week course with organised activities aiming to encourage safety and confidence in the water whilst having fun. In the leisure pool, Thursday 12.30-1.15pm (3 months-1 year) and 1.15-2.00pm (1-2 years). Gym and Swim for ages 2-3 and 3-4: gym session with range of activities followed by water session in the leisure pool, with games and toys to teach basic swimming skills. Wednesday(3-4s) and Thursday (2-3s) 11.00am-12.30pm. For children 4 years plus, classes run after school and on Saturday mornings, termly for 10 week period. You have to book and pay in advance, in person. Good luck on getting and keeping a place – you'll need it!

Culverhay Sports Centre
✉ Rush Hill
☎ 477235 (office hours)
☎ 480882 (after 5pm and weekends)
Classes for children from 5 years, after school and Saturdays.
Parents in the water with less experienced swimmers. Also pre-school classes and life-saving classes. 10 week terms.

Splashers
☎ 447319
Lessons for 3 years+, held at Newbridge School, Prior Park College and Kingswood School. Half-hour or hour long classes, 4-8.30pm during term time. Fees payable termly in advance.

Tennis (Short Tennis)
The 'fun and easy way' to learn basic tennis strokes, using a lighter racquet and soft ball. A useful progression to real tennis for young children.

Excel Coaching
✉ Royal Victoria Park
☎ 425066
Sessions for children from 5 years old. 10 week terms, payable in advance. Classes after school and on Saturday mornings.

Trampolining
Bath Trampoline CLub
☎ Secretary 0117 9325061
Held at Bath Sports Centre, ages 2 to adult. Recreational fun and exercise plus squad for local competitions. Saturday mornings, Tuesday and Friday nights from 5.30pm.

Activities and Clubs

SATURDAY SPORTS CLUBS
Saturday Kidsport
- Culverhay Sports Centre, Rush Hill
- ☎ 477235 (office hours)
- ☎ 480882 (after 5pm and weekends)

Age 8+. Every Saturday throughout the year, 9.30am-12.30pm, variety of sporting activities.

OTHER ACTIVITIES

AFTER SCHOOL CLUBS
Kids Art Club
- St. Mark's Community College, Larkhall
- ☎ 330665 / 337447

Fun art sessions with all materials provided for 4-12 year olds. Wednesday and Thursday from 3.45-5.15pm. Ring for current prices and availability.

Mews Play Club
- Carfax Hotel, Great Pulteney Street ☎ 462089

For children aged 4-11. Monday to Friday, 3-6pm. School collection from Widcombe, St John's, Bathwick and Walcot schools. Pay half-termly in advance. Also open 8.30am-6pm during school holidays (see **Holiday Activities**).

Mulberry House
- High Street, Bathampton ☎ 339843

School collection and children's activity centre. Children 4-11 years collected from 13 schools in the area, given tea and offered a range of activities. 3-6.30pm. Also open 8.30-6.30pm during school holidays. Breakfast Club: from 7.15am. Children given a good breakfast and taken to school.

Newbridge After School Club
- Newbridge Junior School, Charmouth Road
- ☎ 429647

For children aged 4.5-13. Monday to Friday, 3.15-6.00pm. Juice and snack provided. Range of activities on offer. Open during school holidays, 8.30am-6.00pm. Fees weekly in advance. Social Services Registered.

Northside Club
- St Stephen's Centre, Lansdown Road ☎ 314392

Run by a Youth Worker on Tuesday 3.20-5.30pm for 9-11 years and Friday 7.30-9.30pm for 11-14 years. Please ring for details.

Park School
- Weston Lane
- ☎ 421681

Pre-school (from 8.15 am) and after-school sessions (3.30-5.45pm when parents collect) with a qualified teacher at this independent school. Varied activities according to age group; drink and a biscuit provided.

Percy Pack
- Percy Community Centre, New King Street ☎ 313946

Full day-care for children in a play scheme setting. Full variety of activities (see Holiday activities). Children 4.5-12 years. Also in term time, 3-6.00pm school collection from St. Andrews, Parkside Infants, St. Stephens, Widcombe Infants and Juniors. Also school holidays, 8.00am-6.00pm. Book in advance.

Walcot Montessori After School Club
- 9 Grove Street
- ☎ 465752

5-10 year olds, 3.30-5.30pm daily in termtime. £4.50 per day. Art, crafts, drama, computing, games, outside play in fine weather. Pick-up service from St. Stephen's, Widcombe and Bathwick St. Mary Primary Schools.

WASPS (Weston All Saints Primary School) After School Club
- ☎ Janice Roberts 421786 for information.

COMPUTERS
Whizzkidz
- ☎ 466178

Computer aided learning using the latest multimedia computer technology to bring to life the core Curriculum subjects of Maths English and Science, along with an understanding of computer and keyboard skills. For 5-13 years, classes in central Bath.

LANGUAGE CLUBS
Escuelita de Bath
- Hillylands, Weston Lane
- ☎ 429647

Spanish classes and an opportunity to learn in a fun way about Hispanic and Latin American culture through videos, books, music, dance, games, films, arts and crafts. For 3-15 year olds. Monday sessions from 5-6pm in term

22 Bath with your Kids

Activities and Clubs

time (£2.50), Saturday classes at the Park School, Weston Lane, Bath from 10.30am - 12.30 pm (£4.50). No classes during school holidays, but excursions and outings are organised. £5 registration fee when child first joins classes.

French Club
✉ Walcot Montessori School, 9 Grove Street
☎ 465752
Learn French through games, activities, role play etc. For children from 5-10 years. Weds. 4-5pm term times only (Costs £5 per session, payable termly).

La Jolie Ronde
✉ 3 Bennett Street
☎ 442564
Saturday workshops (10.30-11.30am) for 4-11 years based on a learning system of books, tapes and videos with songs, stories, games and activities. £4.63 per session. Different approaches for different ages.

NATURE AND ENVIRONMENT
Bath Environment Centre
☎ 460620
Youngsters can learn about their environment in a fun way using colour and books in a friendly atmosphere. Organises workshops, such as 'Exhaustion', 'Building a car of the future' and 'Making a giant board game'.

Gardening and Nature Club
✉ Bath Organic Group Demonstration Garden, Victoria Park Allotments
☎ 212116
Children's workshop for children aged 7-14 held one Saturday every month during the Spring and the Summer.

The Wildlife Trust
✉ Willsbridge Mill, Willsbridge Hill, Bristol
☎ 0117 9326885
Events held most of the year for children of 5 years+ with adults, at Willsbridge Mill and other venues. Book in advance. Members of Wildlife Trust get reduced rates to most events. During the school holidays children can visit the Mill for activity sessions and Wildlife Discovery Days are available for play schemes and other groups.

Westonbirt Woodpeckers Club
✉ Westonbirt Arboretum
☎ Kevin Beckett 01666 880220
For ages 6-12 years with their parents. Meets last Sunday of month, varied activities: artwork using natural objects, learning about wild animals and birds, scavenger hunts etc. Open to members of the club only. About £6 per child.

Wildlife Watch
☎ 862528
For ages 7 and over. Meet once a month at Bath Environment Centre in winter for fun activities. In summer some wildlife watches are organised.

SOFT PLAY CENTRES
Baskervilles
✉ Burnham Road ☎ 339991
See main listing under **Sports Activities, Gymnastics**.

Boomerang
✉ Bowerhill Trading Estate, Melksham (follow signs to Sports Centre)
☎ 702000
Open all year 10am-6pm. Separate baby area 0-3 years approx. Main and climbing areas for kids up to 1.5 metres (approx age 10). Non members £2.50, members £2. Family membership £14.95 (first day free). Cheaper rates on week days. Café has baby food. Baby changing.

Brokerswood
✉ Westbury ☎ 01373 822238
Soft play area within woodland park (see **Trips and Jaunts**). Open daily 10am-5pm ages 6 months-6 years. Have to pay entrance to park (£2.50 adults), but soft play area free during week and 50p per child at weekends.

Explorers of the Lost World
✉ 39 Brislington Hill, Bristol
☎ 0117 9831343
Daily 10am-7pm. Up to 12 years, separate area for under 4's. Monday-Friday 10am-3pm under 4's only, £2 per child. All other times £2.90 per child per hour (hourly rate only applies when busy). Under 2's free. Watch your kids from café. Highchairs. Baby changing for men and women. Great for a wet afternoon – can get hot and busy. Also hosts children's parties.

Bath with your Kids 23

Activities and Clubs

YOUTH GROUPS

Beaver and Cub Scout groups
☏ Avon County Scouts 01454 613006
Beavers for boys and girls, 6-8 years and Cubs for children 8-10 years, but in practice they are mainly boys. Crafts and creative work, sports, outdoor activities and hiking. Groups are located throughout Bath.

Boys Brigade
✉ 2nd Bath Company
☏ Mr Fitch 429359
'Anchor Boys' (5-8years) Monday 6.15-7.15pm, 'Juniors' (8-11 years) Friday 6.15-7.35pm and 'Seniors' (11-18 years) Friday 7.40-10.15pm. Meet at Weston Free Church. Arts, crafts, sailing, expeditions, music and a marching band. Also work towards Duke of Edinburgh Awards.

Boys Brigade also at Midsomer Norton:
☏ Mr Jakins 01761 414992

Brownies and Rainbows
☏ Bath Division Commissioner 314201
☏ Bath District Commissioners: North: 425297 South: 868642 East: 0117 9863856 South East: 338404 South West: 465653
Rainbows for girls 5-7 years, Brownies ages 7-11 years. Also Guides 10-14/15 years and Rangers 14-18 years. Games, painting, crafts, singing, sport, outdoor activities including camping. Groups are located throughout Bath, often sponsored by churches.

CYC
✉ Christadelphian Church Hall,
56 New King Street
☏ 313656
Church-based youth group, but welcomes non-church members. Age 7-14 years. Mixed activities including crafts, cookery, ball games, bible study, swimming and outdoor activities. Opportunity to join church camp in summer. Friday 7-8.30pm, term times only.

Girls Brigade
☏ 01761 416515
'Explorers' (5-8years), 'Juniors' (8-11 years), 'Seniors' (11-14 years) and 'Brigaders' (14+). Meet at Moravian Church, Coronation Avenue, Wednesday 6.30-8pm. Christian organisation, welcomes children from all denominations. Activities include sports, games, arts, crafts, hobbies, music, camping and competitions.

Junior Gateway Club
☏ 834854
Integrated youth club for both able-bodied and disabled young people aged 7-19 years. Wednesdays 5.30-7.30pm at Centre 69, Penn Hill Road, Weston. Swimming, skittles, discos, sports, crafts, parties, camping weekends and outdoor pursuits.

Red Cross
☏ Mrs Gundry 420696
Junior Red Cross for children 6-11 years, Youth Red Cross for 11-16s. They meet in Bath on Thursday, 6.30-7.30pm at Red Cross House, 55 New King Street. Choice of 9 courses, visits, games and projects. Training on First Aid and how to deal with emergencies.

St. John Ambulance
☏ 01761 417763/01761 412854
'Badgers' for 6-11's, Cadets for 11's plus. Meet at St. John's Headquarters, Pulteney Mews, on Friday. Badgers 6-7.00pm and Cadets 7-8.15pm. First Aid, welfare activities, crafts, sports, games, outdoor pursuits including camping and hobbies. Older members work towards Duke of Edinburgh awards.

Woodcraft Folk
☏ 334386
'Elfins' (6-9 years), 'Pioneers' (10-12 years). Creative activities plus games, camping, rambling, orienteering with a great emphasis on the environment and international and racial harmony. Cooperative rather than competitive activities. Monday at St Bartholomews Church Hall, Oldfield Park and Thursday at St. Marks School, Larkhall.

YMCA
✉ Broad Street
☏ Ivor Vernals or Peter King 460471
Saturday mornings 10-12.30 term time only for children 5-12 years. Activities include: arts, crafts, drama, music and use of indoor sports hall for team and non-competitive games. Pay weekly or take out Junior Membership and pay reduced fee.

Activities and Clubs

HOLIDAY ACTIVITIES

Bath Area Play Project
☎ 313946
Centre 69, Penn Hill Road
Culverhay School, Rush Hill – mornings only, for special needs children only (book in advance).
Foxhill Community Centre, Hawthorne Grove
Moorlands Infant School, Moorfields Road
Odd Down Youth Centre
Oldfield Park (book in advance)
Reg Symes Memorial Hall, Batheaston
Riverside Youth Centre, London Road
Roundhill Centre, Mount Road
Southside Youth Centre, Kelston View
The Hut, Hinton Close, Twerton

Play Scheme sites open from 10am-12.30pm and 2-4pm most weekdays in August. Some sites open at Easter and Christmas. For children 5-16 years and they're free! Organised on a drop-in basis so children can come and go as they please. Activities, often based around weekly themes include art, crafts, sport and outings as well as specialist workshops such as poetry, video and drama. Children with special needs are mostly integrated into the neighbourhood schemes, but there is also a specialist group. It's worth visiting sites to check that they suit your child's needs.

Bath Library Summer Programme
☎ 480110
Craft and reading activities throughout summer holidays for children 4+. Places by ticket only (nominal cost), on sale Monday before term ends. Further information available mid-July.

Children's Summer Fun
✉ Parade Gardens ☎ Sarah Giovannini 396021
Organised by the Leisure Services Department of Bath & NE Somerset Council, children's entertainment (puppets, jugglers, magicians etc) throughout summer holidays. Monday-Friday 2.30pm for 40 minutes-1 hour. Free for residents with proof.

CHURCH CLUBS
Many churches run a club in school holidays, which are usually open to everyone. Check with your local church for details.

Bath Abbey
☎ 422462
One week in August, 5-11 year olds.

Emmanuel CofE
✉ Apsley Road ☎ 427720
5-10+ year olds.

Fosse Way Community Church
✉ Fosse Way Junior School, Odd Down ☎ 835228
February half term, 4-11 year olds.

Hay Hill Baptist Church
✉ The Paragon ☎ 422604
Every Tuesday in August, 5-13 year olds.

St Lukes
✉ Wellsway ☎ 311904
August holiday club in church hall.

St Phillip and St James
✉ Odd Down ☎ 835228
October half term for 4-11 years, in church hall.

Activities and Clubs

Walcot Methodist Church Hall
☎ 464371
Most school holidays, for ages 7 plus.

Widcombe Baptist Church
☎ 316358
Holiday club once or twice a year for children from 3 years.

Loud and Proud Youth Theatre
☎ Oscar Stringer 01249 653785
Weekly drama, dance, video production and day-long animation workshops during summer in grounds of Sheldon Manor. Drama and Dance workshops include 5 days of theatre games, dancing, singing, improvisation etc. Create and perform an original piece of theatre on Friday evening of each week. Video workshops: process of writing, creating storyboard, acting and filming. Each child gets opportunity to use camera, direct and use sound equipment. Book in advance.

Mews Play Club
✉ Carfax Hotel, Great Pulteney Street
☎ 462089
All school holidays and half terms. 8.30am-6pm for ages 4-11 years. Structured activities and trips. Book and pay in advance.

Musicale Holidays
☎ 01582 460978
One week non-residential music course held in August at Monkton Combe School. All ages and abilities. Bands and orchestras etc. for 7-16 year, music activities for 5-9 years for children who do not yet play an orchestral instrument.

National Children's Wind and Chamber Orchestra
☎ Administrator 01582 713333
For children 10-15 years. Entry by audition, for wind, brass and percussion players. Held in Autumn. Also run course at Easter.

Percy Pack
☎ 313946
Full day-care for children in a play scheme setting. Activities as above (see Bath Area Play Project). For ages 4.5-12 years. After School Club and collection service, see *After School Clubs* above.

YMCA
✉ Broad Street
☎ Ivor Vernals or Peter King 460471
Summer fun days for 5-12's, one week in August 10am-4pm. Arts and crafts, sport, games, competitions and music. Bookable in advance.

HOLIDAY SPORTS COURSES
Bath Sports Development
☎ Lynda Deane 396456
Holiday sports courses during all school breaks for children 5-15 years. Various venues in Bath and surrounding area. Netball, hockey, gymnastics, table tennis, basketball etc. Courses last 1, 2, 3 and 5 days.

Culverhay Kidstuff
✉ Culverhay Sports Centre, Rush Hill ☎ 477235 (office hours) 480882 (after 5pm and weekends)
Age 8-15, weekdays 10am-4pm during school holidays. Payable daily. Trampoline, badminton, swimming, team games, football, hockey, tennis, assault courses etc.

Kingswood School
✉ Lansdown Road
☎ 447148
Ages 5-14, courses run during Easter and Summer holidays. Book in advance on weekly basis. 9.30am-3.30pm Monday-Friday. Children are divided by age into small groups and participate in a wide variety of sports. Cricket, fencing, gymnastics, short tennis, pop-lacrosse, rugby, trampolining and team activities. Programme for younger children includes play activities.

King Edwards School
✉ North Road, Combe Down
☎ 481370
Sports activities including tennis, judo, mountain-biking, trampolining etc. Ages 7-13 for two weeks in summer. Book and pay in advance for one week course. Brochure available in March.

Splash Summer Play Scheme
✉ PC Ian Moore, Avon and Somerset Police
PO Box 37, Valley Road, Portishead,
Bristol BS20 8QJ
Two schemes during four weeks of the summer, one in Bristol and one in Bath. For ages 10-15 years. Sporting and leisure activities and day trips. Bookable in advance.

Annual Events

Bath has a good selection of events and activities throughout the year which you and your children can enjoy. Not just the balloon flights, firework displays and duck race, but much more – definitely something for everyone.

We recommend that you phone to confirm before travelling to an event because sometimes details are changed at the last minute.

JANUARY

Pantomimes at various locations in Bath. See **Entertainment – *Theatres*** for details.

FEBRUARY

Bath International Literature Festival
☎ 462231
Some events and story telling for children. Best to book well in advance. Pick up leaflet in library for full details.

APRIL

Henry Roger's Fun Fair
☎ 01454 772494
Royal Victoria Park during the Easter holidays. Can end up expensive if your children want to try every ride/stall but great fun. 4 years+.

MAY

Spring Flower Show
☎ 448433
Royal Victoria Park over May Bank Holiday weekend. Accompanied children under 16 free. Free Horticultural Workshop (5-11 years) run by Bath Area Play Project. Children's competitions. Free WRVS crèche with provision for breastfeeding mothers.

Bath Festival Opening Ceremony
☎ Festival Office 462231
First Friday night of the festival, at dusk in grassy area below Royal Crescent in Royal Victoria Park. Band, fireworks, candles.

Bath Fringe Festival
☎ Fringe Office 480079
Phone for details of children's events.

Bath Children's Festival
☎ Fringe Festival 480079
In Royal Victoria Park on late May Bank Holiday weekend.
Usually includes children's theatre, clowns, magicians, puppeteers, jugglers, dancers, workshops in hat, mask and badge making, dance, song, drama, puppetry, circus-skills. Also has inflatables, swingboats, roundabouts, talent show.

Bath Balloon Festival
☎ Parks Department 448433
First three days of Bath Festival. Mass daily ascents.

Bath International Kite Festival
☎ 427441
Held on Lansdown Playing Fields. Lots of kites to watch, take your own, plenty of room to fly it and loads of interesting stalls. Last weekend of Bath Festival.

Henry Roger's Fun Fair
Royal Victoria Park, Whitsun half-term. (See full listing under ***April***).

Annual Events

RAC Classic Car Run
☎ 01753 681736
Royal Victoria Park. Sunday of late May Bank Holiday weekend.

American Civil War Display
☎ 460503
American Museum, Claverton Down, Bath in mid-May. Civil war re-enactment.

Royal Bath and West Show
☎ 01749 823211
Shepton Mallet. 4 days during Whitsun half-term. Large-scale event. Masses of displays and demonstrations, sheep shearing, baby animals, rare breeds, horse jumping, small fairground by village green, Morris dancing, Town Criers. Good food and drink to sample and buy. WRVS creche and changing facilities. Buy tickets in advance from agents in Bath and save money.

Band Concerts
☎ Parks Department 448433
In Parade Gardens, Royal Victoria Park, Sydney Gardens and Alice Park begin in May and continue throughout the summer. (See **Parks and Play Areas**)

Annual Duck Race
☎ 465659
Held in late May Bank Holiday Weekend. 100,000 plastic ducks will be launched above Pulteney Weir in May 1997, but may be less in following years. Organised by Bath Area Rag to raise money for Muscular Dystrophy.

June

American Indian Weekend
☎ 460503
American Museum, Claverton Down, Bath in mid-June. Dance and music.

BURP
☎ 824212
Sponsored Cycle Ride for Children in Royal Victoria Park. Park is closed to traffic for the day. Prizes and cup to be won.

Bath PPA Fund raising Day
☎ 315073
Royal Victoria Park during National Play Week (mid-June). Bouncy castle, tombola, stalls run by local toddler and playgroups.

July and August

Independence Day Displays
☎ 460503
American Museum, Claverton Down, Bath, on weekend nearest to July 4th. The Crown Forces of 1776 give colourful demonstrations of drill and way of life of infantry men and artillery.

Children's Entertainment
☎ 448433
From 2.30pm daily throughout the Summer holidays in Parade Gardens. Leaflets giving full programme available from Library, Parade Gardens and Tourist Information Centre. Entrance to the park free to Bath and North East Somerset Residents. Telephone for further information. (See **Parks and Play Areas** and **Entertainment and Entertainers**)

Bristol International Balloon Fiesta
☎ 0117 9223978
Ashton Court Estate. three day event at beginning of August. Mass daily ascents craft displays and entertainment.

Glastonbury Children's Festival
☎ 01458 832925
4 day event over August Bank holiday weekend. Organised by Children's World.

Toddlers Week at Bristol Zoo
☎ 0117-973-8951
First two weeks in July, lots of activities for preschool children. Special rates for groups.

September

Bournemouth to Bath Run
☎ 01985 214910
Royal Victoria Park is the end venue. Afternoon of 1st Sun in September. Up to 200 historic commercial vehicles.

28 Bath with your Kids

Annual Events

International Kite Festival
☎ 0117 9772002
Normally second weekend in September. Ashton Court Estate, Bristol. A mass gathering of spectacular kites of all shapes and sizes.

Frome Cheese Show
☎ 01373 467271
(Tourist Office - closed during winter months) Shaw Field, Frome. 3rd Wednesday of September. Agricultural show with displays, craft stalls.

Frome Carnival
☎ 01373 461625
Saturday following Cheese Show. On Wessex Carnival circuit (Trowbridge, Warminster etc.) Special children's procession in afternoon.

Bath Film Festival
☎ 333851
Some workshops/activities for children.

Avon Valley Railway, Willsbridge
☎ 0117 9327296
Normally 2nd Sunday in October, Thomas and friends day. Ride on Thomas the Tank engine and his friends, lots of stalls, fairground rides, bouncy castle, etc.

OCTOBER

Free week
☎ 477000
For Bath and North East Somerset Residents, during half-term. Free entry to many local museums and galleries, workshops (book in advance). Leaflet giving full details of events for children and museum/galleries opening hours, is available at many outlets including Tourist Information Centre and the Library.

Bath University Rag Procession
☎ 465659
Last Saturday in October. At 12 noon floats assemble for judging at obelisk in Royal Victoria Park. 2pm floats depart to tour city for 2-3 hours.

Apple Day
☎ 477662/460620
2nd/3rd Saturday in October at Parade Gardens. Lots of apple fayre, apple games, orchard displays, exhibitions, face painting, story telling and other activities.

NOVEMBER

Bonfire Night Displays
Bath Recreation Ground (November 5th) and Bath University (Saturday nearest November 5th).

Bath University Stunts Day
☎ 465659
Wednesday following Rag procession. Fun and games in town to raise money for charity.

Midsomer Norton Carnival
☎ 01761 415334
Part of a circuit which begins in Bridgwater on Thursday nearest November 5th. Reaches MSN a week later then continues to Wells, Glastonbury and ends in Weston-super-Mare.

Bath with your Kids 29

Annual Events

December

Avon Valley Railway, Willsbridge
☎ 0117 9327296
Weekends throughout December, Santa Special with ride, gift from Santa and mince-pies.
(See **Trips and Jaunts**)

Bristol Zoo
☎ 0117-973-8951
Live nativity scene with Father Christmas in Grotto, various dates in December.

Christmas Water Carnival
☎ 0117 9223521
Bristol City Docks on the Saturday before Christmas. 12 noon-9pm. Christmas markets, bands, carol singing, jazz, illuminated boat procession and major firework display. Free, with collections for charity.

East Somerset Railway
☎ 01749 880417
Railway at Shepton Mallet. Santa Special with ride, gift and refreshments.
(See **Trips and Jaunts**)

Marshfield Mummers
☎ 891469
Boxing Day at Marshfield market place at 10.30am Carol singers and band. 11am-12 noon. Mummers perform up the street. Pagan play depicting the end of winter and the coming of spring. Dressed today in newspapers (originally leaves were worn).

Baby and Toddler Groups

Baby and Toddler groups cater mainly for children up to 4 years. They are usually organised by groups of parents, Health clinics, or church members for the benefit of those living in their local area (you do not have to be a church member to go along). They offer an excellent opportunity for young children to meet others of their own age, and the chance to play with larger pieces of equipment in more space than is available in most homes. Groups generally have ride-on toys, baby toys, push-alongs etc. as well as drawing, playdough and puzzles. Other activities may include painting, sand play, water play, dressing up, singing, dancing, playing musical instruments, listening to stories, going on outings etc. It's also a good opportunity for meeting other parents. A small charge is usually made for tea/coffee, squash and biscuits, and to cover rent and equipment. The groups are listed by area and have all been recommended by local parents, but this is by no means a complete list. To find out about other local groups, ask your health visitor or NCT organiser or look for details in shop windows, newsagents and churches. Most groups accept children with special needs but usually there are no special facilities.

BATHEASTON, BATHFORD AND BATHWICK

Bathford Toddler Group
✉ The Parish Rooms
Wednesday 10am-12pm, 0-3's. £1, includes drinks, average 20-25 children. Friendly meeting place with child centred singing and creative activities.

Methodist Church Hall
✉ Northend
☎ 858378
Tuesday 9.30-11.30am, 0-3years, average 20 children, cost 50p. Run by parents. Well equipped group.

St. John's Church Hall
✉ St. John's Road (opposite fire station)
☎ 466375
New group starting 1997. Phone for details.

Teddy Bear Club
✉ St. Swithens C of E Church, Bathford
☎ 466375
Activities, songs, drawing etc. Run by church every other Tuesday 2-3.15pm. Under 5's. Everybody welcome.

Toddlers Service
✉ St John the Baptist Church, Batheaston
☎ 858539
Wednesday fortnightly, 10.30-11.30am. Activities and music. Refreshments. Free, all year.

BLOOMFIELD AND ODD DOWN

Beechen Cliff Methodist Church Hall
✉ Shakespeare Avenue, Bear Flat
☎ 425230/332006
Monday 2-4pm, all year round except bank holidays and school holidays. Average 20 children, cost 70p per family. Various craft activities, singing, musical instruments. Church affiliated but everybody welcome.

123 Toddler Group
✉ Hillside Hall, Monksdale Road
Thursday 10-11.30am, average 30 children, cost 60p, plus 10p each additional child. Painting, drawing, dressing up, music, singing, dancing. Well equipped.

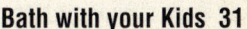

Baby and Toddler Groups

Chatterbox
✉ St. Luke's Church Hall, Wellsway
☎ 311904
Alternate Thursdays 9.15-10.30 under 2's, 10.30 onwards under 5's.
Well equipped, craft activity, group singing. Run by church, lots of helpers.

St. Philip and St. James Church
✉ Frome Road
☎ 835228
Tuesday 1-3pm, 0-5 years, cost £1.25 a year plus 50p a week.
Small friendly well organised group.
Outdoor activities in summer, outings, story time.

The Salvation Army
✉ Oolite Road, Odd Down
☎ 401926
Thursday 9.30-11am. Cost 50p, has story and nursery rhyme time.

CAMDEN, LANSDOWN, LARKHALL AND FAIRFIELD PARK

St. Stephen's Toddler Group
✉ St. Stephen's Centre, Lansdown
☎ 480920
Monday 9.30-11.30am, cost 60p.
Activities include a craft activity, rhymes or singing. Excellent selection of toys for all ages. Storytime in a quiet room. Pleasant, modern premises. Friendly, well organised, caring parent-run group. Ramped access.

Hay Hill Baptist Church Hall
✉ The Paragon
☎ 422604
Tuesday 10-12.00pm, open to under 5s, average 20 children, cost 80p.
Plenty of ride-on toys, playdough, dressing up, tapes, painting, plus music and singing time. Refreshments available throughout morning. Run by church members, but open to all.

St. Saviour's CofE Church
✉ St. Saviours Road, Larkhall
☎ 311637
Wednesday 10-11.30am, 2-3.30pm, average 25 children. Many toys, craft activity, friendly. Can get crowded, but has separate baby area. Level access from Holland Road. Run by church but open door policy.

Walcot Methodist Church
✉ Nelson Place East
☎ 461991
Wednesday and Friday 10-11.45am, 30+ children, cost 50p per family which includes coffee and squash. Lots of toys, climbing frame, slide, trampoline, plus cutting, sticking and painting. Run by church.

St. Mary's RC Church
✉ Julian Road
☎ 314586
Thursday 10.30am-12pm. Friendly, informal group.

Fairfield Park Health Centre
✉ Tyning Lane, Camden Road
☎ 446630
Offers various parentcraft classes which are ongoing and changing according to the needs of parents in the area. For precise information contact your health visitor or phone.

CENTRAL

Forum Toddlers
✉ The Forum, St James Parade
☎ 463556
Entrance: Corn Street, through green door, ring bell. Thursday 10am-12 noon. Ages 0-5, 50p. Stories, crafts, music, theme each term and outings. Very friendly group.

Open House Toddler Group
✉ Manvers Street Baptist Church
☎ 461600
Tuesday 10-11.45am, under 3s only, average 20 children, cost 40p. ☎ 01761 433417. Thursday, under 5s, ☎ 852064/834874. Easy access down ramp at left hand side of church (towards sorting office). Art activity each week, end with songs and rhymes. Run by church. Carers and nannies welcome. Coffee lounge upstairs has facilities for children.

Parents and Tots
✉ Salvation Army, Bath Citadel, Green Park
☎ 400051/873987
Thursday 10-11.30am, termly. Cost 30p includes drink and biscuits.

32 Bath with your Kids

Baby and Toddler Groups

Percy Community Centre
✉ New King Street
☎ 423014
Runs groups in response to demand. Phone for details.

St. Johns RC Church
✉ Parish Hall, South Parade
☎ 464471
Tuesday 10-11.30am, free.

Walcot Church Toddlers Group
✉ Snow Hill Christian Centre
☎ 425590
Thursday 10am-12 noon, termly. Cost 40p.

NEWBRIDGE AND WESTON

Little Saints Toddler Group
✉ All Saints Church Centre, High Street, Weston
☎ 447663 (mornings)
Wednesday 9.30-11:30am and 1-3pm, Friday 9.30-11.30am, 0-5 years, average 20 children, cost 50p plus £2 yearly registration fee. Two rooms. Activities include sponge painting, playdough, story time, puppets, singing, dancing, musical instruments. Church link: pram service once a month on a Friday morning.

Tigerlily Parent and Toddler Group
✉ Weston Methodist Church Hall, Kennington Road, Weston
☎ 314386
Monday 9.30-12pm, 0-4years, cost 60p (inc. refreshments). Singing, playdough, drawing, stories, dressing up, summer outings etc. Separate area for babies. Ramp to hall. Well organised, run by committee, not church related. Jumble sales, clothes sales, photographer visits.

Weston Musical Toddler Group
✉ Centre 69, Penn Hill Road, Weston
☎ 331140
Monday 9.30-10.45am, 0-5years, average 25 children, cost £1.25 including coffee. Very popular with waiting list. Ring first and speak to Mary. Main activity is 45 minute music session with general play and refreshments beforehand. No creche facility, parents must stay.

St. John's Parent and Toddler Group
✉ St. John the Evangelist Church, Upper Bristol Road, (near Fina garage)
☎ 310532
Thursday 10-11.45am, 0-3years, average 30 children, cost 50p. Annual Teddy Bears' picnic. Birthday card and Christmas present for each child. Christmas celebration and visit to church to see crib.

OLDFIELD PARK AND BEAR FLAT

Noah's Ark Club
✉ Ascension Church Hall, Oldfield Park
☎ 317747
Every Wednesday 10-11.45am. Includes singing and playing instruments.

Oldfield Park Methodist Church
✉ The Triangle, Oldfield Park
☎ 425230
Wednesday 10-12noon, average 35 children. Plenty of equipment but no organised activity. Run by church members.

Oldfield Park Baptist Church
✉ The Triangle, Oldfield Park
☎ 330055
Wednesday 1.30-3pm, 15-20 children. Run by church. Wide selection of toys but no organised activity. Coffee available.

SOUTHDOWN

Parent and Toddlers
✉ The Roundhill Project, Mount Road
☎ 400010
Monday and Friday 9.30am-12pm. Cost 50p, everyone welcome.

Southdown Toddler Group
✉ Southdown Methodist Church, The Hollow
☎ 310470
Wednesday 10-11.30am, 0-5 years, cost 80p. Well equipped, separate area for babies. Drawing, craft, music. Thursday 10am-1pm Care and Friendship Group. Lunch for nominal charge. Church affiliated.

Baby and Toddler Groups

TWERTON

Southside Parent and Toddler Group
✉ Southside Youth Centre, Kelston View, Twerton ☎ 423218
Friday 10am-12pm. Parents run an ongoing programme of community issues. Cost 50p, includes refreshments.

The Hut
✉ Hinton Close, Twerton
☎ 400018/401618
Wednesday 9am-12pm. Everyone welcome. Costs 50p, includes refreshments. Teenage Mums n' Tots group starting Wednesday pm.

The Salvation Army Church and Community Centre
✉ Haycombe Drive, Whiteway
☎ 422673
Tuesday afternoons, phone for details.

Twerton Baptist Church Hall
✉ Mill Lane, Twerton
☎ 336271
Thursday 1-2.30pm all year, 0-3's (older in holidays), 15 children, cost 70p. Sandwiches and cakes. Finger painting, drawing, story, singing.

WIDCOMBE AND COMBE DOWN

St. Mark's Toddler Group
✉ St. Mark's Community Centre, St. Mark's Road, Widcombe ☎ 332567
Tuesday 10am-12pm, average 55 children, cost 80p plus 20p per extra child. Includes refreshments. Baby room, lots of toys and equipment, church yard used in summer. Books, painting, sand pit, singing. Plenty of space for rushing about, letting off steam. Special events, like second hand toy sales. Everyone expected to clear up on rota basis.

Widcombe Toddlers
✉ Widcombe Baptist Church, Pulteney Road, Widcombe
☎ 316358
Thursday 10-11.45am, cost 75p includes coffee, juice and biscuits. Excellent selection of toys. Craft activity, playdough, water-play, quiet room with books and puzzles. Singing session at end followed by ride-on trucks and bikes.

Church link, monthly bible service and stories, group is open to all. Very friendly and well organised. Separate area for babies.

Combe Down Toddler Group
✉ Church Rooms, The Avenue, Combe Down ☎ 833914
Tuesday 9.30-11.30am, usually open during half-terms, 6 months-3 years, cost 40p. Two rooms, separate area for babies. Arts and crafts, singing, ride-on toys and trampoline. Also play house and book corner. Small, friendly group largely local parents. PLA affiliated.

Before and After Club
✉ Church Rooms, The Avenue, Combe Down ☎ 777272
Thursday 10am-12 noon, all year round, 0-3 years, cost 30p. Baby clinic every week. PLA affiliated.

Foxhill Toddlers
✉ Hawthorn Grove, Foxhill ☎ 832137
Thursday 9.30-11.30am, cost 50p. Refreshments, bikes, slide, trampoline, garages, small toys and books. Outside safe area.

Southstoke and Midford Toddlers
✉ Southstoke Village Hall (next to Packhorse) ☎ 835993
Thursday 10.30am-12pm, termly. Small friendly group. Craft activity and singing session.

St. Andrew's Church Hall
✉ Hawthorn Grove, Combe Down
☎ 837378
Tuesday 9.30-12pm, mainly under 3s. Refreshments 50p: saved for Christmas party and summer outing. Separate area for babies. Climbing frame, tricycles, sit and ride, puzzles, books, playdough. In summer, outside area is used. Caring church group, run by church members.

STEINER TODDLER GROUP

Seedlings Toddler Group
☎ 891730
Friday 10am-12pm, for 0-3 and half years, £2-£5 contribution. "Homely environment where parents and children learn new crafts and skills to enrich their lives."

Child Care

CHILDMINDERS

Childminders care for your child in their own home. If they work for more than two hours a day, they must be registered with the County Council. They can usually care for up to three children under 5 and up to three children between 5 and 8 years. To be registered, they must be in good health, have a safe home (checked by a Fire Officer) with adequate play and rest space, toys and play materials and be able to provide good quality practical care and a well balanced diet for children. Social Services Department will also check that none of the adults resident in the house has ever been convicted of an offence against children. Before choosing a childminder it is worth visiting a few and asking if you can spend some time with them to make sure that your child will be happy there. You should ask to see their certificate of registration and read their conditions of registration – also check whether they have insurance cover for your child as this is compulsory.
If you are looking after a friend's child for more than two hours a day, for payment, and the child is under 8 years of age, registration under the 1989 Children Act with the County Council is compulsory.

Registration and Inspection Unit

✉ Riverside, Temple Street, Keynsham, Bristol BS18 1LA ☎ 01225 394333
Hold lists of childminders, playgroups, playschemes, after school clubs, nurseries, crèches etc. Will also supply details about becoming registered as a childminder.

Bath and Wandsdyke Childminders Group

☎ 332946/837733/01761 470087
The Bath Childminders' Group gives its members the chance to get to know other childminders, offering each other help, support and advice. They also offer help to parents looking for a childminder.

Parents at Work (formerly Bath Working Mothers Group)

☎ 429647
Monthly meetings held, often with speakers. Offers a chance to meet other parents who work outside the home, and can sometimes help with information concerning childminders, nanny-shares etc. Good support group for working parents.

NANNIES

A Nanny cares for your children in your own home, on a part or full-time basis, living in or out. The recognised qualification is the N.N.E.B. Diploma in Nursery Nursing, but not all parents ask for this. It is well worth interviewing several nannies before deciding who is suitable for your child. Decide in advance what you will expect the nanny to do - maybe, some

Bath with your Kids 35

Child Care

housework or evening babysitting - and discuss this at the interview. If you are employing a nanny for more than a few hours per week, you will need to add payment of Income Tax and National Insurance to their basic rate. Contact the Tax Office who have a simplified payment scheme available for small employers.

H.M. Inspector of Taxes

Royal Mead 4/5a Railway Place, Bath
☎ 328300

The cheapest way to find a nanny is to advertise in shop windows or through the local newspapers (Evening Chronicle/Star ☎ 444545/0891 311513).
Alternatively you can contact the following agencies who will charge a placement fee ranging from about £50 for finding part time staff to £150 for full-time permanent staff. They will also find temporary staff. It is up to you to interview, follow up the references supplied and sort out payment and contracts.

Bathtime Nannies

7 Bloomfield Park, Bath BA2 2BY ☎ 422789

Featherbed Nannies

46 Bath Hill, Keynsham, Bristol BS18 1HG
☎ 0117 9860710

Mulberry Nannies

High Street, Bathampton ☎ 423221

BABYSITTERS

There are numerous locally organised babysitting circles in and around Bath where a group of people who live fairly close together organise reciprocal babysitting, usually on a debit/credit token basis. These circles tend to limit their numbers and do not advertise. Your NCT organiser or Health Visitor may be useful people to ask. Otherwise, why not start your own by placing a notice in a shop window or church noticeboard?

36 Bath with your Kids

Eating Out

We have listed restaurants and cafés both in and out of Bath, which we've enjoyed visiting with our children. Since the last edition, we are pleased to note that children's interests are being considered more often in the provision of facilities in restaurants - we have highlighted places which offer baby-changing facilities, highchairs, and children's portions. Some have activities for older children - ranging from colouring sheets with crayons provided and books to read, to tractors to climb on and animals to look at. There are still lamentably few places offering baby-changing facilities - and even fewer making them available to men. Some are waking up to the needs of parents though - and realise that in attracting parents they are giving a significant boost, not only to their current sales, but also, in introducing children to the joys of eating out, to their sales when those children grow up to become the customers of the future.

KEY TO SYMBOLS

🧸 recommended for babies – have baby changing and highchairs.

🔍 colouring etc./entertainment for children.

CITY CENTRE

Bathtub Bistro
✉ 2 Grove Street ☎ 460593
Open Monday 6-11pm, Tuesday-Friday 12-2.30pm, 6-11pm, Saturday and Sunday 12-11pm. Busy, informal bistro with more space than it looks and varied menu. Daytime snacks, plenty for veggies. Children's special seat and small portions available. Room for folded buggies.

Bath Spa Hotel 🧸 🔍
✉ Sydney Road ☎ 444424
Choice of two restaurants – the very pricey Vellore and the Alfresco offering unusual Mediterranean food. Kids menu and highchairs. Fairly expensive, but a real treat for a special occasion. Can pay for day membership and use Laurels Spa (possibility of paying extra for use of on-site nursery).

Bath Tandoori
✉ 36 Broad Street ☎ 425924
Open daily 12-2pm and 6pm-Midnight. Basement Indian restaurant - excellent food. Friendly but not especially geared up to very young children. Lunchtimes 25% discount.

Bella Pasta 🧸 🔍
✉ 13 Milsom Street ☎ 462368
Open daily 12-11pm. Speciality pizza/pasta restaurant which is very child friendly. Children's menu, baby changing facilities and highchairs available. Easy access for buggies.

Binks
✉ 17/18 Cheap Street ☎ 466563
Open daily 8am-10pm. Full range of snacks and meals. Fast service. Children's menu and highchairs available. Easy access for buggies and toilets downstairs with space to change a nappy. Popular with tourists, in Summer it's nice to sit outside in Abbey Churchyard.

Bloomsbury's
✉ 7-10 Manvers Street ☎ 311755
Open Monday-Saturday, 10.30am-8 pm, Sunday 4-8pm (open later for drinks). Cafe/Restaurant, coffees, teas, cakes, snacks and traditional pub food. Lively, friendly atmosphere. Children's portions, loos and highchairs available.

Boating Station
✉ Forester Road, Bathwick ☎ 466407
Open daily 12-3pm. Café at Victorian boating station serving teas, snacks, light lunches and Sunday roast. Lovely views of river. No highchairs but small portions available. Boatman Restaurant serves more formal meals every evening except Sunday.

Eating Out

A L F R E S C O

Enjoy simple and distinctive seasonal dishes in an informal and relaxed atmosphere.

Choose from just a starter and a glass of wine, a dessert and coffee or a full three courses.

CHILDREN FRIENDLY!

We welcome your children for lunch and dinner (until 7.00pm) and provide children's menus, highchairs and colouring posters to keep them amused!

FOOD FOR THOUGHT...

Ravioli of Ricotta Cheese, Fresh Spinach and Smoked Bacon, Basil Gratin

Asian Peppered Beef Stir Fry with Rainbow Vegetables, Salad and Rice

Cadbury's Chocolate Burger with Mango Chips

and specially for the children....

Action Man Special

Space Age Treat

THINK ABOUT IT! THEN CALL
01225 444424

THE BATH SPA HOTEL
SYDNEY ROAD BATH BA2 6JF

Bonghy Bo
✉ 14 Upper Borough Walls ☎ 462276
Open Monday-Saturday 9am-6pm, Sunday 10am-6pm. Light meals, soups, snacks. 20 steps up from street, plenty of space in courtyard. No highchairs, toilets cramped but fine for older kids.

Il Bottelino
✉ 5 Bladud Buildings ☎ 464861
Open daily 12-2pm, 5.30pm- midnight (Sunday 6.30pm-midnight) Italian family run child-friendly restaurant. Fairly cramped inside, toilets downstairs but great for older children. Highchairs for younger ones. Excellent food!

Burger King
✉ 4 Cheap Street ☎ 319169
Open Sunday-Thursday 10am-10pm, Friday 10am-11pm, Saturday 9am-11pm.

Café Jass
✉ Great Western Antiques Centre, Bartlett Street ☎ 445448
Monday-Saturday, 10am-4.30pm, Wednesday 8.30am-4.30pm. Good for teas, snacks and cakes. Easy access, lots of space. Toilets downstairs.

Café Rene/Le Parisien
✉ Shires Yard (Broad Street) ☎ 447147/469999
Monday-Saturday 8am-5.30pm, Sundays in Summer only. Side-by-side small French cafés serving snacks and light meals. Room for buggies and space for toddlers to run around outside. Highchairs available. Toilets upstairs.

Cafe Rouge
✉ Upper Borough Walls ☎ 480042
Open daily 10am-11pm, 10.30pm Sundays. French bistro food with interesting kid's menu e.g. breaded salmon fingers. Highchairs, easy access, colouring etc. for children. Lively child-friendly atmosphere but no space to run around.

Caffe Martini
✉ 9 George Street ☎ 460818
Open lunch Monday-Saturday 12-2.30pm, Sunday 12.30-2pm, dinner Monday-Sunday 6-10.30pm. Cheerful Italian pizza, pasta, meat restaurant. No highchair but friendly, spacious and provides children's portions.

Caffe Piazza
✉ The Podium Northgate Street ☎ 429299
Monday-Saturday 8.30am-11pm, Sunday 10am-

Eating Out

10pm. Snacks and good value lunch specials. Children's menu and highchairs. Ask for key for baby changing. Access via lift or escalator. Light, spacious and airy, also fountains and fish.

Caffe Uno
⊠ The Empire, Grand Parade ☎ 461140
Open daily 10am-midnight, Sunday 11.30pm. Stylish and bright with good views of Pulteney Bridge and Sham Castle. Extensive Italian menu, plenty for veggies and wonderful puddings! Children's menu, spacious toilets, baby changing, highchairs. Puzzles on back of kid's menu, crayons provided. Access up steps but staff will help. Take away available in times of crisis!

California Kitchen
⊠ The Podium Northgate Street ☎ 471471
Open Monday-Saturday 9.30am-10pm, Sunday 11am-9pm (but ring first to check as it depends on the time of year). Spacious Californian chargrill serving up-market US brunch style food. Good value all day breakfast until 5.30pm. Kids menu, highchair and baby changing (ask for key). Access via lift or escalator.

The Canary
⊠ 3 Queen Street ☎ 424846
Open Monday-Saturday 9am-8pm, Sunday 11am-5.30pm. Proper English tea room with tempting display of homemade cakes also light meals, snacks, under 12's menu. Highchairs available. Limited space for folded buggies. Adult atmosphere - perhaps not the ideal place for boisterous children!

Carwardine's Coffee House
⊠ The Podium Northgate Street ☎ 460088
Open Monday-Saturday 8.30am-6pm, Sunday 11am-5pm. Coffee House serving speciality coffees and teas, also sandwiches and snacks. Access via lifts. Has highchairs. Toilets/baby changing facilities in Podium (get key from till). Fairly cramped inside for buggies but outside terrace with good views of Pulteney Bridge.

Chaplin's Restaurant
⊠ 4 Pulteney Bridge ☎ 447310
Open daily 9.30am (approx)-11pm (lunch 12-3pm, dinner 6-11pm). French/Italian bistro. Good value set lunch, evenings a la carte. Room for buggies. Children's portions.

Demuths Vegetarian Restaurant
⊠ 2 North Parade Passage ☎ 446059
Open Monday-Saturday 9am-10pm Sunday 10am-9pm. Imaginative and varied vegetarian and vegan food, seasonal specials. Children's menu and highchairs. No smoking throughout. Booking essential at weekends. "Tiny premises make this an unlikely child-friendly place to eat, but the friendly staff and superb food compensate!"

Evans Fish Restaurant
⊠ 6 Abbeygate Street ☎ 463981
Open Monday-Wednesday 11.30am-6pm, Thursday-Saturday 11.30am-8.30pm. Classic fish and chip restaurant. Highchairs and kid's menu available. Easy access for buggies but limited space once inside.

Firehouse Rotisserie
⊠ 2 John Street ☎ 482070
Monday-Saturday 12-2.30pm, 6pm-10.30pm or later. Busy, lively restaurant with an interesting Californian/Tex-Mex influence. Good value at lunchtime. Room for buggies, and children's portions available. Open for coffee Monday-Saturday 10-11.30am and Saturday afternoons.

Footlights
⊠ The Podium, Northgate Street ☎ 480366
Open Monday-Saturday 10am-11pm, Sunday 12-10.30pm. Large, bright Tex-Mex restaurant also burgers, sandwiches and gooey desserts. Child-friendly with highchairs, baby changing (ask for key) and children's menu. Busy at weekends.

Garfunkels
⊠ The Empire, Orange Grove ☎ 461465
Open daily 10am-11.30pm. Spacious American-style restaurant. Kid's menu, goody packs (watch toddlers with tiny pieces), baby changing facilities and highchairs available. Only drawback is access - up steps, but staff will help on request. Better value at lunch time than in the evening.

Green Park Brasserie
⊠ Green Park Station ☎ 338565
Open Tuesday-Saturday 10am- late evening, Sunday 10.30am-3pm. Friendly informal brasserie in the old station building. Live jazz at weekends. Highchair and split portions. Loo with enough room to change a baby on window ledge. Especially recommended for jazz at Sunday lunchtime.

Bath with your Kids 39

Eating Out

Haagen Daz
11 Old Bond Street ☎ 464629
Open daily 10am-11pm. Fabulous ice creams, also limited choice of cakes and cookies. Table service or take-away. Toilets downstairs with baby changing facilities. Highchairs. Relaxed, family-friendly atmosphere, totally non-smoking. Rather pricey, but worth it!

Holbourne Museum Tea House
Sydney Place ☎ 466669
Open 1st week in February to Christmas. Tuesday-Saturday 11am-5pm, Sunday 2pm-5pm. Wide range of homemade cakes, beverages, snacks and lunches. Limited space inside, outside areas with benches and tables on lawn. Toilets in museum.

Jazz Cafe
Kingsmead Square ☎ 329002
Open Monday-Saturday 8am-9pm Sunday 10.30am-4pm. Buzzing, cheerful café serving breakfast, snacks, light meals, (chilli con carne and lasagne), sandwiches and teas. Very good value. Easy access for buggies. Newspapers. Toilets. Children's portions and highchair.

Jolly's Department Store:
Milsom Street ☎ 462811
Il Caffe
Open Monday-Saturday 9am-6pm, Sunday 11am-5pm. Cafe in basement serving excellent coffee and snacks. Easy access from Old King Street behind Jolly's. Lots of space for buggies and active toddlers. Highchairs. Toilets upstairs.

Terrace Restaurant
Open Monday-Saturday 9am-5.30pm, Sunday 11.-5pm. Self-service restaurant on first floor - access not easy via very small lift. However staff are helpful. Kid's menu and highchairs available. Separate areas for non-smokers.

Littlewoods
19 Stall Street ☎ 442755
Open Monday-Saturday 9.30am-5.15pm, Sunday 11am-5pm. 2nd floor self-service, easy access via lift. Snacks, light meals, drinks etc. Kid's menu and highchairs. Baby changing room.

McDonalds
38 Southgate ☎ 463764
Open 8am-11pm (Sat. 7am). Can get very busy.

Manvers Street Coffee Shop
Manvers Street Baptist Church
Excellent place to take a shopping-break. Relaxed, child friendly atmosphere, large area at the back with toys where children can be boisterous without disturbing too many people. Snacks, homemade cakes, light lunches etc. Nappy changing facilities. New ramp to left of the building and automatic doors makes access wonderfully easy!

Marmaris
4-5 Grand Parade ☎ 461946
Open daily 12 noon-12 midnight. If you like Turkish food this is the place to come! Delicious middle eastern food, served with typical warmth and hospitality. Very welcoming to children with highchairs and kid's portions available, also free pittas and hummous for the very young. Toilets and baby changing upstairs.

Monks Coffee House
7 Abbey Church Yard ☎ 460759
Open 10am-5.15pm daily. Coffee House serving coffees, teas, snacks and cakes, also light lunches from 12-2pm. Very crowded and busy, especially with tourists. Few tables outside in Abbey Churchyard. Toilets.

The New Moon
Seven Dials (next to Theatre Royal) ☎ 444047
Open daily 11am-11pm. Interesting modern menu with French/Italian bias. Elegant but comfortable and spacious setting. Very easy flat access, highchairs and kid's portions with kid's menu on Saturdays. Good for cakes and coffee, especially in large patio area outside, though watch toddlers as they can escape into road.

No.5 Bistro
5 Argyle Street ☎ 444499
Tuesday-Saturday 12-2.30pm, Monday-Saturday 6.30pm-10.00 or 11.00pm. Good local reputation for interesting food. BYO Monday and Tuesday evenings. Children's portions and highchair.

The Octagon Cafe
Royal Photographic Society, 43 Milsom Street ☎ 447991
Open 9.30am-5pm daily. Coffee and cakes all day, also light lunches. Access tricky for buggies down

Eating Out

long flight of steps. Highchair available. Pricey but pleasant. Non-smoking.

Old Orleans
✉ 1 St.Andrew's Terrace, Bartlett Street ☎ 333233
Open Monday-Saturday 12noon-11pm Sunday 12noon-10.30pm. Large, lively American style restaurant serving Southern, Cajun, Creole food and burgers, fajitas etc. Child friendly with highchairs and separate kid's menu provided with colouring, puzzles and crayons. Lots of stairs but for buggies/wheelchairs phone or ring bell on back door by Woods, Alfred Street.

The Oliver Inn
✉ 9 Green Street ☎ 464666
Open Monday-Friday 12noon-3pm and 6-10pm, Saturday 12noon-10pm, Sunday 12-2.30pm and 6-10pm. Classic English steakhouse. Good value kid's meals and highchairs. Toilets downstairs.

Pasta Galore
✉ 31 Barton Street ☎ 463861
Open daily 12noon-2.30pm and 6pm-10.30pm. Very friendly restaurant serving own delicious fresh pasta and sauces (shop in Broad Street) also pizzas, specials etc. Highchair and small portions available. Garden open when fine.

Peppers
✉ 5-6 Edgar Bdgs, George Street ☎ 465777
Open Monday-Saturday 8am-10pm, Sunday 10am-9.30pm. All-day breakfasts, snacks or meals. Patio garden and tables on terrace. Spacious loos, highchairs and small portions. Colouring for children. Day-times best for families, smoky and crowded in evenings.

Pierre Victoire
✉ 16 Argyle Street ☎ 334334
Open Monday-Saturday 12noon-3pm and 6-11pm, Sunday 12noon- 3pm. French bistro food - very good value menus. Friendly atmosphere. Clip on highchair. Will split portions for children.

Pizza Express
✉ 1 Barton Street ☎ 420119
Open daily 11.30am-12 midnight. Italian pizzeria chain serving delicious pizzas, garlic bread etc. Children enjoy watching the pizzas being prepared and cooked in the oven. Highchairs available. Relaxed, informal and child friendly.

Pizza Hut
✉ 1 Westgate Buildings ☎ 448586
Open Sunday-Thursday 12noon-11pm, Friday 12noon-midnight, Saturday 11am-midnight. Room for buggies. Highchairs, children's menu, bag of goodies. Baby changing for men and women. Friendly, helpful staff and rapid service.

The Pump Room
✉ Abbey Churchyard, Stall Street ☎ 444477
Open daily 9.30am-4.30pm. Restaurant in the beautiful Georgian Pump Room. Unique and elegant atmosphere often with a string quartet playing - a bit pricey but lovely for a treat. Morning coffee, Bath buns a speciality, light lunches, afternoon teas. Highchairs and baby changing facilities available. Families are welcomed.

Puppet Theatre
✉ By Weir next to Pulteney Bridge ☎ 480532
Open daily 7.30am-6pm. Access down many steps from Pulteney Bridge or go round via Grove Street, down slope and back under road. Yummy wholefood cakes, salads, sandwiches, jacket potatoes etc. Good value, ideal for children. Highchairs. Small loo. Non-smoking. Can sit outside but not much room. Puppet Shows are now only held at Weston for parties. (See **Entertainment and Entertainers**)

Rascals Bistro
✉ 8 Pierrepont Place ☎ 330201
Open for Lunch Monday-Saturday 11.30am-2.30pm, Dinner Sunday-Thursday 6–10.30pm, Friday/Saturday 6-11pm. Lively vaulted cellar restaurant with child friendly staff. Bistro-style menu, good value set lunches and dinner. Highchair and children's portions available. Access down flight of stairs. Great atmosphere with blues and soul music.

Regency Café
✉ York Street
Open Monday-Saturday 8am- 4pm, Sunday 10am-4pm. Busy café. Breakfasts, snacks, teas and light meals. Nearest toilets at The Pump Room. Good value. Take away available and can eat in Abbey Churchyard with pigeons!

The Rickenbacker Food Co.
✉ 10 Upper Borough Walls ☎ 444255
Open daily 12noon-10.30pm (last orders).

Bath with your Kids 41

Eating Out

Busy, lively restaurant serving burgers, chilli, pasta, salads, etc. One of the best places to go with a family. Easy access for buggies. Highchairs, extensive children's menu and toys to play with. Free baby food and feeding equipment provided. Baby changing for both men and women. Breastfeeding no problem. Best to book in evening as very popular.

The Royal Pavilion Café

✉ Pavilion, Victoria Park ☎ 448860
Open daily 8.30am-5pm. Airy, spacious café serving cakes, ice-cream, snacks and lunches. Also Sunday lunch. Access via lift. Totally non-smoking, highchairs and baby changing facilities. Very handy for a trip to Victoria Park playground or just a walk in the park.

Sally Lunn's

✉ North Parade Passage ☎ 461634
Open Monday-Saturday 10am-6pm Sunday 12noon-6pm. By day small, busy tea rooms in what is reputed to be Bath's oldest house. Famous for its Sally Lunn buns and popular with tourists. Small loo, highchairs. Museum in cellars with amazing stalagmites and stalactites.

Scoffs

✉ Kingsmead Square ☎ 462483
Open Monday-Saturday 8am-9pm. Excellent wholefood snacks, lunches and cakes. Small inside but a few pavement tables outside. Non-smoking, highchairs, small loo downstairs.

Seafoods

✉ 38 Kingsmead Street ☎ 465190
Open 11.30am-11.30pm Monday-Saturday. Bright and cheerful fish and chip restaurant. Highchairs and children's portions available. Toilets. Good location for cinemas.

La Tarte Flambee

✉ 12 George Street ☎ 460033
Open Tuesday-Saturday 12 noon-2.30pm and 6-10.30pm. Sunday 12 noon-2.30pm and 7-10pm. Good value French food. Child friendly atmosphere. Highchair, children's menu and table in Ladies for baby changing.

Tilley's Bistro

✉ 3 North Parade Passage ☎ 484200
Open Lunch Monday-Saturday 12 noon-3pm.

Dinner every evening 6.30-11pm. Has a strong local following for its delicious French and English home-style cooking. Easy access, baby changing facilities, highchairs and children's portions available. Very pleasant, child friendly.

The Walrus and the Carpenter

✉ 28 Barton Street ☎ 314864
Open Monday-Saturday 12-2.30pm, 6-11pm, Sunday 12-11pm. Bistro with extensive menu including plenty of veggie options, will split portions for children. Space for folded buggies, highchairs available. Small toilets. Need to book in evenings. Families warmly welcomed!

Waterstones Coffee Shop

✉ Milsom Street ☎ 448515
Open Monday-Saturday 10am-5.30pm, Sunday 12noon- 5pm. Tea shop with delicious cakes, snacks and light lunches on first floor (lots of steps, no lift). Small portions, will warm bottles etc. Loos with very small ledge to change baby.

The Wife of Bath

12 Pierrepont Street ☎ 461745
Attractive bistro serving lasagne, fish, veggie options etc. Large portions and wonderful puddings. Access down steps is tricky but service is welcoming and friendly. Small patio in courtyard. Highchairs and children's portions.

Window Arts Centre Café

✉ St. James Memorial Hall, Lower Borough Walls
☎ 421700
Open Tuesday-Saturday 10am-6pm. Café serving teas, vegetarian snacks and light meals. Highchair and children's portions. Access tricky down steps. Convenient during childrens events at Arts Centre. Phone for details.

Woods

✉ 9-12 Alfred Street ☎ 314812/422493
Open Lunch Monday-Sunday 12 noon-3pm, Dinner Monday-Saturday 6-11pm. Delicious Anglo-French food, light, spacious surroundings. Excellent value set menus. Baby changing, highchairs and children's menu. First Sunday of the month a clown entertains for 2 hours at lunchtime. Children very welcome

Eating Out

OUTSIDE CITY CENTRE

American Museum
⊠ Claverton Down ☎ 460503
Tuesday-Sunday 2-5pm (Easter-November 1st). Pleasant cafe, delicious cakes, cookies, drinks and ice creams. Tables inside or out with stunning views over valley. Outside plenty of room to run around. Highchairs and baby changing. Tea rooms only open to those visiting grounds or museum (minimum. entrance fee £2.)

The Boathouse
⊠ Newbridge Road ☎ 482584
Open Monday-Friday 11am-3pm and 5.30-11pm, Saturday 11am-11pm, Sunday 12noon-10.30pm. Large restaurant by the river. Very family orientated. Highchairs, kid's menus, baby changing facilities (for men and women) and spacious toilets with a child size toilet and low sink! Great family room and garden with play area including swings and slide. For adults good selection of real ales and occasional live music.

Canalside Cafe
⊠ Lock Inn Cottage 48 Frome Road, Bradford-on-Avon ☎ 868068
Open daily all year (except Christmas Day) 9am-6pm. Café by canal serves big breakfasts, teas, snacks, lunches, bangers and mash, cream teas and more! Also hires canoes and bikes.

Chewton Cheese Dairy
⊠ Chewton Mendip ☎ 01761 241666
Open daily 10am-4.30pm. Delicious lunches, yummy cakes and puddings with mountains of clotted cream from the dairy. Relax while downing your cream tea – the kids will be entertained watching the cheese making or reading the books provided. Self-service, highchairs, obliging staff, attractive pine-clad setting. Loos downstairs across the courtyard. A good place to stop off on a journey to Wells/Wookey Hole.

The Cornerstone Coffee Shop
⊠ 1 Upper Lambridge Street, Larkhall ☎ 319450
Open Monday-Friday 9.15am-5pm, Saturday 9.15am-4pm. Spacious, friendly café. Serving very good value teas, ice creams, homemade cakes and snacks, free coffee refill. Room for buggies, highchair, baby changing, toilets and books. Well worth a detour after a visit to Alice Park.

Fordside Tea Gardens
⊠ 111 Winsley Hill, Limpley Stoke ☎ 722115
Open all year daily 11am-6pm (hours may vary). Homemade food served in family run tea gardens. Views of Limpley Stoke valley and lovely garden. Buggies/bikes need to be lifted over a few steps into the garden. Large hut in case of bad weather, but garden is the main attraction.

Hillier Garden Centre
⊠ Whiteway Road ☎ 421162
Open Monday-Saturday 10am-5pm, Sunday 10am-4pm. Cafe in large garden centre with lovely views. Serves light lunches, homemade cakes and drinks. Tables inside and out. One highchair. Toilets. Don't forget to visit the tropical fish next door.

The Old Bell
⊠ Abbey Row, Malmesbury ☎ 01666 822344.
Enjoy a peaceful meal while children go to on-site crèche, 10am–6pm and playground. Book in advance. Run by the same people as Woolley Grange (below).

The Old Mill Hotel
⊠ Tollbridge Road, Batheaston ☎ 858476
Open daily 11am-11pm. Riverside restaurant serving teas, coffees, bar meals and full restaurant menu. Lovely views of river and water wheel. Children welcome in restaurant (highchairs available) and bar if well behaved. Can also sit outside in the garden, but keep an eye on toddlers near water. Lots of ducks!

People and Planet
⊠ Avon Third World Centre, Swinford Mill, Swineford, Near Bitton ☎ 0117 932 3505
Open Wednesday-Saturday 10.30am-5pm, April-December. Teas, coffees and delicious homemade cakes. Extremely good value. Also light lunches. Access easy. All non-smoking. Self-service. Lovely garden but children must be supervised (there is a pond and low wall to river and weir). Peaceful atmosphere so not for the over exuberant! Clean spacious toilets with room to change babies.

Prior Park Coffee Shop
⊠ Prior Park Garden and Pet Centre, Prior Park Road, Bath ☎ 427175
Open Monday-Saturday 9.30am-4.30pm, Sunday 10.30am-4.30pm. Bright, roomy café, teas, snacks,

Bath with your Kids 43

Eating Out

cakes, light meals. Highchair. Toilets. Excellent garden and pet centre.

Red Lion Harvester
✉ 468 Wellsway, Odd Down ☎ 832487
Open Monday-Friday 12-2.30pm, 5.30-11pm. Saturday–Sunday 12-11pm. Excellent service, helpful staff. Highchairs and children's menu. Clean toilets with pull down changing unit.

The Rockery
✉ North Road, Combe Down (opposite Rainbow Woods) ☎ 833274
Easter-October, Tuesday-Sunday 10am-6pm. Teas, cakes, snacks, lunches. Beautiful gardens, plenty of room for running around. Tables inside and out. Lovely place to relax in Summer. (See **Walks**)

Stables Restaurant
✉ Dyrham Park ☎ 0117 937 4293
Open April-end October 11am-5pm, closed Wednesday/Thursday. November, December and March open weekends only 12noon-4pm. Waitress service restaurant also teas, cakes and snacks. Easy access and friendly atmosphere. Toilets. For park visitors only (£1.60 adults, 80p kids) National Trust members free.

Teasels Tearooms
✉ Avon Villa, Avoncliff, near Bradford-on-Avon ☎ 863867
Open daily Easter-end September 10am-5.30pm. Winter, weekends only. Lovely garden with animals, just off canal towpath at Avoncliff. Café serving teas, homemade cakes and snacks.

Woolley Grange Restaurant and Hotel
✉ Woolley Green, Bradford-on-Avon ☎ 864705
Open daily 7.30am-10pm. Wide range of meals including nursery meals for children at 12 noon and 5pm. Crèche with nanny on site in separate barn - open to diners. Here is the freedom to have your Sunday lunch (set price for 3-course meal) in blissful peace, while your children have theirs and are entertained. Access no problem, highchairs, very helpful staff. Baby-changing in Ladies' loos. Book in advance. Also has an outdoor swimming pool. Excellent reputation far and wide – a real treat but at a price.

Two luxury hotels
welcoming children of all ages. Both hotels have individually decorated rooms where children can be accommodated in their parents' room for free or take one of our family or inter-connecting rooms, all priced accordingly. They have nurseries open from 10am until 6pm every day and nannies are happy to amuse the children for all or part of the day. Children can eat together at specially arranged times for lunch and dinner. All this guarantees a relaxing and enjoyable stay for parents who may choose to relax in the gardens or in one of the many lounges with big open fires and comfy sofas.

Woolley Grange is the country house standing in 14 acres of beautiful countryside. It has an outdoor pool, lawn tennis, badminton and croquet.

Prices start at £99 for a double room; family rooms from £190

Bradford-on-Avon
Wiltshire BA15 1TX
Tel: (01225) 864705
Fax: (01225) 864059

The Old Bell is the town house adjacent to the ancient Abbey in the historic town of Malmesbury. Lovingly tended gardens at the back of the hotel are the perfect place to relax with a glass of Pimms and a good book.

Prices start at £85 for a double room; family rooms from £130

Abbey Row, Malmesbury
Wiltshire SN16 0AG
Tel: (01666) 822344
Fax: (01666) 825145

Education – Pre-School and Primary

There are no rules about the names different types of registered preschools can use, so any group may call itself a 'nursery' 'nursery school' or 'playgroup'. The important thing to remember is not what a group calls itself, but what type of place it is.

For further information on 'choosing what's best for your child' phone 0345 543345 for a free leaflet or write to DFEE Freepost 402, London W!E 2DE.

Day Nurseries and Nursery Schools

Nurseries have to be registered with the County Council and are visited every year by a Social Services Officer to check standards of care and safety are maintained. If nurseries are open all day, the requirements are more stringent and include provision of a rest area, a good kitchen and laundry facilities. Minimum staff/children ratios are maintained and at least half the staff must be qualified and have recent relevant experience with pre-school children.

This list is not exhaustive. The majority have waiting lists and so it is worth arranging a visit well in advance of when you want your child to attend and putting their name down for the one that suits you best. All have a minimum requirement of two half-day sessions up to a maximum of five full days a week, unless otherwise stated. All those listed have equal opportunity policies, but vary in their interpretation of what this means. All can cater for special needs to some degree but would want to discuss individual needs with parents. You can expect most, or all of the following activities: painting, modelling, drawing, listening to stories, writing, sand and water play, playing musical instruments, gardening, talks from visitors, dressing-up, outings, singing, dancing, reading, drama, cooking, watching television.

There is one Bath & North East Somerset Council Day Nursery in Bath with severely restricted places. You must be referred through a Health Visitor or Social Worker. For information see Advice and Support.

Abacus Day Nursery
✉ Stirtingdale Farm, Corston View
☎ 837639
Ages 2-5years. Open 8.30-5.30pm Monday to Friday. Closed Bank Holidays, Easter, Summer and Christmas 2 week breaks. Fees paid monthly in advance. 12 children. Ratio of staff to children 1:6. Outside: large enclosed grassy area surrounded by green fields, Shetland ponies and other farm animals. **Reading • writing • numeracy:** children work in small groups to allow more individual attention.

Education – Pre-School and Primary

Bath College of Higher Education Day Nursery
✉ Corston Drive, Newton Park ☎ 873701 xt 284
Age 0-5 years. Open 8.45am-4.45pm all year round. Fees paid monthly in advance. Ratio staff/children under 2's 1:3, 2-3 1:4, 3-5 1:8. Maximum 15 per session. Outside: grass with play equipment. **Reading • writing • numeracy:** Children over 3 use The Highscope Format to develop essential pre-school skills.

Bloomfield Nursery School
✉ 15 Bloomfield Road ☎ 421572
Age 3 years+. Open 8.30am-5pm. Termly (but open half terms) Fees paid monthly in advance. Ratio of staff/children: 1:5, maximum of 18 children per session. Outside: paved area, lawn. **Reading • writing • numeracy:** through play activities at first - but more formal later.

Caterpillars Day Nursery
✉ Royal United Hospital, Weston ☎ 824462
Age 3 months-5 years. 7.15am-5.30pm all year except Bank Holidays. Mainly for hospital staff.

Minimum attendance: two half days. Fees paid four weekly in advance. Ratio staff/children: Toddlers 4:1; Preschool 8:1. Maximum of 24 at session. Outside: patio with cover and grass area and high fence. **Reading • writing • numeracy:** Pencil control, activities, teach name writing.

First Steps Nursery
✉ Dominion Road, Twerton ☎ 444791
Age range 2-5 years. Open 8am-6pm, only closed Bank Holidays. Fees paid weekly or monthly in advance. Ratio staff/children, 2 years 1:4, 3 years 1:8. Outside: enclosed area and garden. **Reading • writing • numeracy:** 'Desirable Learning Outcomes' leading to National Curriculum Key Stage One.

Fledglings Kindergarten
✉ Corsham Arts Centre, Pound Pill, Corsham, Wiltshire ☎ 891730.
Age range 3.5-6.5years. Open 9.30-3.00, termly. Recognised member of the Steiner Schools Fellowship. Minimum attendance 3 mornings per week, 9.30am-1pm. Maximum attendance 4 mornings and 3 afternoons. Deposit in advance. Ratio of staff/children: 1:9 or 1:10. Maximum of 20. Outside: Playground, sand-pit and simple structures. Many country walks and outings.

Happy Days Nursery
✉ The Rosary, Culverhay School, Rush Hill ☎ 429989
Age 0-5 years. Open 8.30am-5.30pm all year, closed 2 weeks at Christmas and 2 weeks in August. Fees paid monthly in advance. Ratio of staff/children, 2-3's 1:4, 3-5's 1:8. Maximum 30 children in class. Outside: enclosed grass and hard area. **Reading • writing • numeracy:** they have two qualified primary teachers who follow National Curriculum.

Hickory House
✉ Stokeside, Midford Road ☎ 832139
Age 2.5-4years. Open 8.30am-5.30pm termly. Minimum attendance two and a half day sessions. Fees paid termly in advance. Ratio of staff/children under 3's 1:5, 3-4's 1:8. Maximum 15 children in a class. Outside: safe, enclosed garden with playhouse, sandpit and slide. **Reading • writing • numeracy:** Pre-reading, writing and maths incorporated into activities.

Steiner Education

THE FLEDGLINGS KINDERGARTEN

for children 3½ - 6½ years

Offering your child a gentle welcome to education

Please contact
Joy de Berker 01225 891730

Education – Pre-School and Primary

Hopscotch Nursery School
✉ 98 Wellsway ☎ 448191
For children aged 2.5-5years. Open 9am-4pm termly. Fees are paid monthly in advance. Ratio of staff/children: 1:4. Maximum number of children at session, 20. Outside: soft play area.
Reading • writing • numeracy: writing patterns leading to letters. Phonics and number work.

Jabberwocky Montessori Nursery School
✉ 7 Lansdown Crescent
☎ 330070
Age 2-5 years. Open 8.00am-6.30pm 50 weeks per year. Children may attend during school terms and/or holiday playschemes. Minimum attendance 3 mornings or 2 afternoons. Fees paid termly (payment by instalments available). Outside: large garden.

Mulberry House
✉ High Street Bathampton
☎ 339843
Age 0-2.5 years. Open 8.15am-3/4pm all year. 6pm holiday time. Specialist baby department for 0-18 months. Staff/children ration 1:3. Fees paid weekly in advance. Outside: lawn and patio, safe and enclosed. Two nursery classes for 2.5-5 years: termly with optional holiday care provided. **Reading • writing • numeracy:** qualified primary school teacher.

Pinnocchio Day Nursery
✉ The High Street, Weston
☎ 336710
Age 18 months-5 years. Open 7.30am-5.30pm all year. Hours negotiable. Fees paid monthly in advance. Ratio of staff/ children: 1:4, maximum of 24 children at a session. Outside: playground.

Playbox Nursery
✉ 20 Gloucester Road ☎ 332579
16 months to school age. Open 8am-5.30pm, all year round. Attendance: full week, full time only. Fees paid weekly or monthly in advance. Ratio staff/children under 2s 1:3, 2-3years 1:4, over 3years 1:8. Maximum of 24 at a session. Outside: dry play area and grassed area. **Reading • writing • numeracy:** learning from commencement of nursery through play, continuing by using games to become familiar with letters and numbers. Use work books in the final year before learning phonics, adding, subtracting, copying etc.

Tadpoles Nursery
✉ The Avenue, Combe Down
☎ 837717
Age 2.5-5years. Open 8.30am-5.30pm all year. Four weeks holiday per year. Affiliated to Combe Down Primary School. Minimum attendance of 1 session. Ratio staff/children 1:5. Maximum of 20 at a session. Outside: large walled garden with grass and patio. **Reading • writing • numeracy:** structured activities provided when children show readiness. Lots of reading and phonetic skills taught with a balanced approach.

The City of Bath College Day Nursery
✉ Avon Street
☎ 328649
For children aged 2-5 years. Open 8.30am-5.00pm, closed during some holidays. Fees paid weekly. Ratio of staff to children: for ages 2-3 years: 1:4, ages 3-5 years: 1:8. Maximum of 18 children at a session. Outside: Astroturf. **Reading • writing • numeracy:** run a pre-school group each morning for 3-5 year olds.

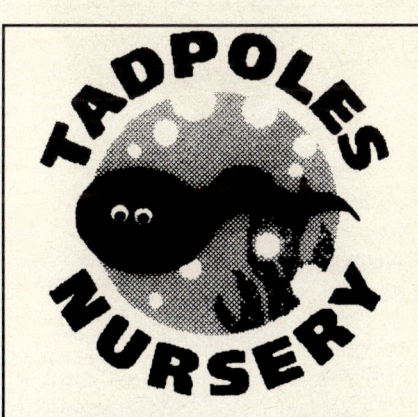

TADPOLES NURSERY

Combe Down, Bath
Open 8.30am - 5.30pm
Education and care for
2½ to 5 year old children
Telephone (01225) 837717
Nursery Vouchers accepted

Bath with your Kids 47

Education – Pre-School and Primary

The Kemble Nursery
✉ Bath Spa Hotel, Sydney Road
☎ 337519
Age 2-5years. Open 8am-6pm all year round. Fees paid four weekly in advance. Ratio of staff to children 1:5. Maximum of 15 children in a class. Outside: large garden and playground. **Reading • writing • numeracy:** 'Desirable Learning Outcomes' as set out by S.C.A.R. Learning through play in preparation for school.

The Kinder Garden
✉ 12 Catharine Place
☎ 426857
Age 2-4years. Opening hours: 8.30am-5.30pm, Monday to Friday 46 weeks per year. Fees paid weekly in advance. Ratio of staff to children 2years 1:4, 3-4years 1:6. Maximum number at a session: 20. Outside: courtyard with playhouse used throughout the day by small groups. **Reading • writing • numeracy:** play and structured activities. 'Letterland' and a 'real books' approach also used.

The Mews Nursery
✉ Carfax Garden, Henrietta Mews
☎ 332593
Age 18 months-5 years. Open 8.30am-5.30pm, all year. Fees paid monthly in advance. Ratio staff/children under 2's 1:3, 2-3years 1:4, 3-5 years 1:8. Maximum 20 at a session. Outside: enclosed garden, lawn and patio. **Reading • writing • numeracy:** through play.

The Tree House Day Nursery
✉ St Martin's Hospital, Midford Road
☎ 840383
Age 18 months-5 years. Open 8am-6pm all year. Fees paid weekly/monthly in advance. Maximum of 30 children at a session. Outside: enclosed, grassy. **Reading • writing • numeracy:** Pre-school programme.

Victory Pre-School
✉ Victory Christian Centre, Moorlands, Englishcombe Lane
☎ 319635
Age 3-5 years. Open 8.30am-3pm termly. Fees paid monthly in advance. Ratio staff/children: 2:9. Maximum of 9 children at a session. Outside: local park close by and extensive grounds available. **Reading • writing • numeracy:** phonics and letter recognition; coordination skills to build towards reading and writing; number recognition.

Walcot Montessori School
✉ 9 Grove Street
☎ 465752
Age 2.5-7 years. Open sessions and care from 8.30am-5.30pm termly. Paid termly or half-termly. Minimum attendance: three half day sessions. Ratio staff/children: 1.6, maximum of 30 children at a session. Outside: Small garden French taught. **Reading • writing • numeracy:** Children are introduced to all of these and each child is catered for individually.

Weston Park Nursery School
✉ Weston Park
☎ 429439
Age 2.5-5 years. Open 9am-4pm termly. Ratio of staff/children 1:6, maximum of 18 children at a session. Montessori based.

KINGSWOOD DAY PREPARATORY SCHOOL

College Road
Lansdown
Bath
BA1 5SD

Telephone:
(01225) 310468

A CO-EDUCATIONAL SCHOOL FOR PUPILS AGED 3-11

- A caring community
- Good pupil/staff ratio
- Strong extra-curricular programme, music and drama
- Excellent sports facilities at Kingswood Senior School
- Nursery classes for children from the age of 3. Morning, afternoon or full day sessions from 8.15-5.30pm

For further details, please ring the school. We shall be happy to make an appointment for you to visit us.

333209

Education – Pre-School and Primary

Westwood Nursery
✉ University of Bath, Claverton Down
☎ 826518
Age 2-4 years. Open 8.45am-5.30pm all year, closed 1 week at Christmas. Fees monthly in advance. Maximum 24 children per session. Ratio Staff/children 2-3's 1:4, 3-4's 1:8. Outside: spacious grassy area with play equipment. **Reading • writing • numeracy:** basic number and letter recognition, learning through play.

Y Tots
✉ City of Bath YMCA, Broad Street Place
☎ 460471/465448
18 mths-5 years. 8.30am-5.30pm all year. Fees monthly in advance. Ratio of staff/child 1:4, maximum 20 children at session. Outside: small grassy area for use in summer. Sports hall all year round. **Reading • writing • numeracy:** wide range of pre-school activities.

NURSERIES IN INDEPENDENT SCHOOLS

Charlecombe Nursery, The Royal School
✉ Lansdown Road
☎ 313877
Age 2.5-4years. 8.30am-3.30pm sessional, termly. Fees paid monthly in advance. Ratio of staff/children 2-3's 1:4, over 3's 1:8. Outside: soft play area. **Reading • writing • numeracy:** learning through educational play activities.

Monkton Combe Junior School Pre-preparatory
✉ Combe Down
☎ 837912
Age 3-7 years. Open 8.15am-12.30pm. Fees paid termly in advance. Ratio staff/children 1:6. Minimum attendance 5 mornings. Outside: small copse, play equipment, extensive grounds. **Reading • writing • numeracy:** individual teaching, basic skills.

The Garden Nursery, Kingswood
✉ College Road, Lansdown
☎ 310468
Age 3-4 years, open termly 9.15am-12pm and 1.15-3.15pm. Fees paid termly in advance. **Reading • writing • numeracy:** learning through play, uses 'Letterland' and Phonics with carefully chosen activities.

The Paragon School Nursery
✉ Lyncombe House, Lyncombe Vale ☎ 310837
Age 3-4's, 9am-12pm, 1-3pm, lunch available. Fees paid termly in advance. Ratio of staff/children 1:8. Waiting list. Outside: grass area, shared facilities with school, sports hall. **Reading • writing • numeracy:** structured learning activities, phonic based reading.

The Park School (Pre-preparatory for King Edwards School)
✉ Weston Lane ☎ 421681
Ages 3-4years and rising 3's. 8.15am-3.15pm, fees termly in advance. Staff/children ratio 1:6. Outside: enclosed playground. **Reading • writing • numeracy:** Under 5's curriculum as defined by DFEE.

NURSERIES IN STATE SCHOOLS

Fosseway Infant School
✉ Frome Road, Odd Down ☎ 833294

Parkside Infant School
✉ Charlotte Street ☎ 424425

Southdown Infant School
✉ Mount Road ☎ 424950

St Andrews C of E Primary School
✉ Northampton Street, Julian Road ☎ 310135

St Saviours C of E VC Infant School
✉ Spring Lane, Larkhall ☎ 313928

Twerton-on-Avon Infant School
✉ Poolemead Road, Twerton ☎ 423526

Walcot C of E Infant School
✉ Dover Place ☎ 316281

STATE NURSERY SCHOOL ADMISSION POLICY

Children are admitted on or after their third birthday. Attendance is normally part-time, though some full-time places are available at the discretion of the head teacher. Nursery classes in primary schools often admit children from a wider area than that normally served by the school. However admission at this level does not guarantee rights of continued education in the same school.

Education – Pre-School and Primary

PLAYGROUPS

Playgroups generally take children between the ages of 3 and 5 years, although some take rising 3's. Most like children to attend at least two sessions a week. A fee is charged. Parental involvement is usually relied on, during the sessions and in management. Parents (or substitutes, like grandparents) are often expected to help. Playgroups enable children to develop skills of all kinds and give them opportunities to play with children of their own age in stimulating and secure surroundings. Activities usually include painting, drawing, modelling, water-play, sand-play, dressing-up, singing, drama, listening to stories. Some have gardens and offer outdoor activities. Visiting speakers' and trips out may sometimes be included too.

Some have rising 5's sessions specifically for the older pre-school child, where reading and writing are encouraged. Some groups have waiting lists.

Playgroups must be registered with Social Services. To do this they need to fulfil certain criteria, for example adult/child ratios, numbers of qualified staff present at each session, first aider available in the group, and ensuring that health and safety aspects are covered. Most playgroups belong to the Pre-school Learning Alliance.

Bath playgroups are listed by area. We have given the venue and opening times of all the playgroups currently registered with BANES Social Services department.

Up to date lists with telephone numbers for individual playgroups can be obtained by calling: 394333.

BATHAMPTON, BATHEASTON AND BATHFORD

Bathampton Playgroup
✉ Village Hall, Holcombe Lane, Bathampton
☎ 463060
Monday-Wednesday and Friday, 9.30am-12 noon.

Jack and Jill Playgroup
✉ The Burchell Room, Methodist Church, Northend
☎ 858555/858945
Monday-Friday 9.15-11.45am. Rising 5's due to start Friday afternoons.

Bathford Pre-School
✉ Parish Rooms, Church Street, Bathford
☎ 859437
Monday, Tuesday, Thursday 9.30am-12pm.

BEAR FLAT AND OLDFIELD PARK

Beechen Cliff Methodist Church
✉ Bruton Avenue ☎ 423736
Monday, Tuesday, Wednesday, Friday 9.45-11.45am.

Hillside Playgroup
✉ Hillside Hall, Cotswold Road
Monday, Tuesday, Wednesday, Friday 9.30-11.30am. Friday 12.30-2.30pm.

Oldfield Park Baptist Playgroup
✉ Baptist Church Rooms, Moorland Road
☎ 423736/427591
Monday-Friday 9.30-11.45am, 1-3pm.

Stepping Stones Playgroup
✉ Ascension Church Hall, Oldfield Park ☎ 317953
Monday, Tuesday, Thursday, Friday 9.30-11.45am.

CENTRAL

Open House Playgroup
✉ Manvers Street Baptist Church ☎ 469894

COMBE DOWN AND WIDCOMBE

The New Avenue Playgroup
✉ The Scout Hut, The Avenue, Combe Down
☎ 834183
Mon-Fri 9.30-11.45am. Rising 5's Weds and Friday.

Widcombe Acorn Playgroup
✉ St. Marks Community Centre, St. Marks Road, Widcombe ☎ 859505
Monday, Wednesday-Friday 9.30am-12.00pm.

LARKHALL

Larkhall Playgroup Centre
✉ St. Marks School, Baytree Road ☎ 317786
Monday-Friday 9.15-11.45am, and 12.30-3pm.

ODD DOWN AND SOUTHDOWN

Sunshine Playgroup
✉ United Reformed Church Rooms, Rush Hill
☎ 834469/832035/837202
Mon-Thurs 9.15-11.45am, Mon/Weds 1-3pm.

Education – Pre-School and Primary

Barnaby Pre-School
✉ St. Barnabas Church Hall, Mount View, Southdown
☎ 331728
Monday, Wednesday, Friday 9.45am-12 noon.

Opportunity Playgroup
✉ Rosemary Lodge, Wellsway
☎ 835669
Open 10am-12pm (closed Wednesday). For children with mental and physical disabilities, developmental delay and other special needs. A family centre - 0-5's welcome plus their siblings. A wide range of play activities including music and movement, an adventure playground, and a sensory and soft play room (rumpus room). A chance for parents to relax, fosters mutual help and co-operation between parents, friends, staff and volunteers.

Lansdown
Springfield Playgroup
✉ 16 Springfield Place
☎ 422760
Monday-Friday 9am-12 noon.

Twerton
Rainbow Playgroup
✉ Twerton Baptist Church Hall
☎ 400733
Monday-Thursday 9.30-11.45am.

Weston
Weston Playgroup
✉ The Church Centre, High Street
☎ 420696
Monday, Wednesday, Thursday, Friday 9.15-11.45am.

Peter Pan Playgroup
✉ Methodist School Room, Kennington Road, Lower Weston ☎ 445280
Tuesday-Friday 9.30am-12pm, Thursday 12.30-2.30pm for rising 5's.

Combe Park Pre-School
✉ 16 Combe Park, Weston
☎ 332088
Monday-Friday 9.15am-12 noon.

The Pre-School Learning Alliance
☎ 0117 9077073
☎ Local groups information 01761 436548

The Pre-School Learning Alliance is a voluntary organisation registered as an educational charity. Their aim is to enhance the development and education of children under the statutory school age by encouraging parents to understand and provide for their children through play and pre-school groups. The group provides friendly support, advice and information from appropriately qualified and experienced workers. They have regular local meetings and training courses for anyone involved with under fives. They give advice on finance and personal management, health and safety and other sources of help. They produce a selection of helpful leaflets and a monthly magazine. The group also runs an insurance scheme for play and toddler groups and can offer small grants to new and needy groups.

Pre-School Education Voucher System

☎ Information Line 0345 543345

From April 1997 all parents of four year olds will be given a voucher (worth £1100), which they can use for three terms of nursery education at participating nurseries and playgroups (actual terms will depend on when each child has their birthday). At time of writing it is not possible to identify which pre-school establishments will be involved in the scheme. We advise that parents contact nurseries individually. Vouchers will be for use in any State, voluntary and private nursery or playgroup taking part in your area that has places available. In state schools and nurseries the voucher covers at least a part-time place and a full-time place if offered. You will not be charged any fees. In participating private and voluntary groups the voucher covers fees of £1100 a year or £366 a term. If fees are more than this you will have to pay the difference.

Only schools, nurseries and playgroups that meet the conditions specified by the Department of Education will be able to join the scheme. They will have to be registered, and adhere to specific guidelines.

Phone the Information Line for more details (calls charged at local rate).

Bath with your Kids 51

Education – Pre-School and Primary

Primary School Admission Policy

A child whose fifth birthday occurs on or before the first day of a school term must, by law, receive full-time education from the beginning of that term. There is no legal requirement for a school to admit younger children. However, children whose parents live in Bath & North East Somerset may be admitted to school at the beginning of the school year provided that they reach the age of four on or before August 31st of the same year.

First Admission to an Infant or Primary School

✉ PO Box 25, Riverside, Keynsham Bristol BS18 1DN ☎ 01225 395208
You should apply to a school no later than the October preceding the year of admission. It is advisable to check the final admission date as these change from year to year – contact address above. Even if there is an older sibling at the school the younger child must still be registered. If you are registering your child at more than one school you should place such schools in order of preference.

The Appeal System

If a place at your chosen school is unavailable you can appeal under section 7 of the Education Act. The appeal must be made in writing and addressed to: The Director of Education, Admissions and Transport Unit, PO Box 25, Riverside, Keynsham Bristol BS18 1DN You should include the following:

- child's name, address and date of birth
- name of the preferred school
- reasons for preference
- grounds for appeal

The committee will pay particular regard to:
- any siblings already in attendance
- medical, psychological and/or special educational reasons where a particular placement is recommended by the Authority's professional advisors and is accepted as essential by the Authority
- distance from the school
- single-sex and co-educational reasons.

You have a right to appear and speak at the Appeal Committee. If a place does become available at the school after the meeting of the Appeals Committee, priority will be given to children within the area of prime responsibility of the school. (Information obtained from Director of Education, Bath & North East Somerset Council.)

Education Otherwise

Aims to support anyone who wishes to undertake home education. It provides a newsletter, information on the legal situation, help with resources, workshops and ideas. Those interested may wish to read Jean Rendell's book 'School's Out', based on her own family. For further information send A5 SAE to:

Education Otherwise

✉ PO Box 7420 London N9 9SG
☎ 0891 518303

Entertainment and Entertainers

CHILDREN'S PARTY VENUES IN BATH

Parties with home made food and fun are almost certainly the cheapest and most rewarding. However, they're not always practical. If you're planning a party for your children or larger group you might find some of these suggestions helpful. If you need more space, village, sports and community halls can often be hired privately. Any prices quoted here were valid in late 1996, but may have increased - we have left them in merely as a guide. See **Shops** and **Mail Order** to find where to buy party bag fillers, party invitations, themed paper tableware, cake decorations etc.

Alice Park Café
- Alice Park, Lambridge
- 858590 (summer)

Open at weekends during the summer from 1-5.30pm. Can provide a birthday tea. Once tea is finished, children can play in the park.

Baskerville's Gymnastics and Fitness
- Burnham Road, Lower Bristol Road
- 339991

Parties on Saturday 1–3.00pm, 2–4.15pm, 3.30–5.15pm (other times by arrangement). Costs £40, maximum of 18 children. Use of gym equipment, trampoline, bouncy castle, ball pool etc., supervised by trained coaches, plus singing session. Parents provide party tea, held in an upstairs room.

Bath Puppet Theatre
- Weston ☎ 312173

Lively puppet show, huge wholesome birthday tea and chocolate cake, glass of sparkling wine for parents. Flat fee of £25 plus £5.50 per child.
Book well in advance, as it's very popular.

Bath Sport and Leisure Centre
- North Parade Road
- 462563

£35 gets you a choice of 2 dry sports for maximum of 12 children, £40 includes swim as well. Takes children from 7 years. Book 1 month in advance. Hire the Créche room with use of TV and radio for £15.00 and bring your own food, or book a meal in the café.

Caffe Piazza
- The Podium
- 429299

For parties of 10 or more they provide free balloons, party poppers, hats and a cake. Children's menu - price depends on your requirements. Extra charge for clowns, jugglers and entertainers. Book a week in advance if you want a cake. Staff are warm and welcoming. Highchairs available. Easy access by lift and plenty of buggy space.

Combe Grove Manor Hotel and Country Club
- Shaft Road, Monkton Combe
- 835533

Birthday parties can be held in the crèche from 1pm each day. Hire of hall £40, or for two floors £60. Parents provide the food.

Entertainment and Entertainers

Culverhay Sports Centre
- Rush Hill
- 480882

Saturday 2 or 4pm, £32.00 per hour. Any 2 activities from: 5-a-side football, team games, badminton, basketball, hockey, netball, volleyball, table tennis or party games. Activity lasts 30 minutes and is organised by a sports centre attendant. Room for birthday tea at no extra charge. You provide the food. Suitable for 4 years+, maximum 16 children

Evans Fish Restaurant
- Abbey Gate Street
- 463981

10-60 children any afternoon 3-5.30pm. Example price £3 per child, £5 per adult, includes main meal, pudding and drink. Balloons and party hats provided. Can cater for up to 100 and will deliver for up to 300 within a 5 mile radius!

John Rennie
- Sydney Wharf, Bathwick Hill
- 447276

Boat chartered for a 2 or 3 hour cruise. Price varies according to season. Can provide catering if needed and are happy for you to engage a magician or party entertainer. You must provide plenty of adult supervision as you will need to keep an eye on young children who will find water very fascinating.

McDonalds
- Southgate
- 463764

Themed birthday parties run by trained host/hostess who organise games. Guarantee of 1 prize for each child, jungle theme party bags with goodies to take home plus a gift for the birthday child. Birthday tea, cake (ordered in advance for £5.99), mini tour of McDonalds for children. £3.99 per child or £1.99 for package plus cost of food ordered.

Old Orleans
- 333233

If booked well in advance, Ali Alligator will make an appearance at children's parties. Price depends on which food is ordered from special children's menu.

Rainbow Wood Farm
- Claverton Down
- 466366

Open for groups and birthday parties. Will provide party tea and drink plus a tour of the farm, but bring your own cake. Price to be arranged when booking. Wear wellies rather than best party clothes!

Theatre Royal
- Sawclose
- 448844

Birthday tea in the 1805 Rooms for £6 a head. Can provide an entertainer. Teas are usually linked to a pantomime or theatre visit when members of the cast may sometimes come to meet the children.

CHILDREN'S PARTY VENUES OUTSIDE BATH

Boomerang
- Unit 2 Merlin Way, Bower Hill, Melksham
- 702000

One hour in soft play room with host/hostess, birthday tea and drinks for parents. Colour invitations provided plus a Tee shirt for the birthday child. £5.95 per child or £3.50 per head if you provide your own food. See **Activities and Clubs**, *Soft Play Centres* for details of other activities.

Brokerswood and Woodland Heritage Museum
- Westbury, Wiltshire
- 01373 822238

£4.50–5.50 per head depending on choice of food. Price includes scavenger hunt and prize, entry to park, adventureland and museum, party tea for under 6's and half an hour in soft play area. 50p extra for train ride and £2 each for parents who stay.

Explorers of the Lost World
- Brislington, Bristol
- 0117 983143

One hour in the soft play room and party tea. Fast food with pudding. Party bags, hats and masks included and a small gift for the birthday child. Bring your own cake. £6.50 per head.

54 Bath with your Kids

Entertainment and Entertainers

Lulsgate Airport
✉ A38, Near Bristol ☎ 01275 474444
Birthday teas served in the restaurant overlooking the runway. Choice of 3 menus from £3.50 per head. Hats and balloons provided, you supply birthday cake and your own supervision. 50% deposit required when you book.

Monkeys Tweentown
✉ Cheddar ☎ 01934 742270
An indoor padded adventure playroom. £2.25 per child, £2 for under 5's on Wednesdays in term time, before 3.30pm. For £6 you can hire a table for a maximum of 10 children and provide your own birthday tea. Or select food from the menu which offers a choice of hot fast food (£2.20) or sandwiches and cakes (£1.65 or £2.20). Homemade chocolate cake £6. Open 10.30am–6.30pm weekends, Wednesdays and holidays, otherwise 3.30–6pm. Also available for hire at other times by arrangement for groups of 20 or more.

Mrs Pickwick
✉ 70 High Street, Midsomer Norton
☎ 01761 414589
Provides food and drink set out on the table in a pleasant upstairs room with access to music and tapes. Birthday cake can be ordered in advance. Parents organise the games. Costs £30 for 10 children, additional children £2 each.

Norwood Farm
✉ Bath Road, Norton St Philip
☎ 01373 834356
Caters for parties during opening season, mid March–mid September. £4.50 per head which covers entrance fee to the farm, birthday tea in cafe with wholesome home made foods, party bags, balloons and a chance to feed the animals. Pony rides are 50p extra. Parents must organise games. Will also make Animal cakes to order, priced from £9.

Pigs Folly
✉ Cold Ashton, near Marshfield
☎ 891849
Farm on the A420, a few hundred yards east from the roundabout at junction with the A46. Open all year round, parties only held between Easter and September. Costs £5.50 per head, which includes entrance to farm and birthday picnic. Parents provide birthday cake.

Seymours Family Club
✉ 47-49 Barton Vale, Bristol
☎ 0117 9290093
3 hours of entertainment (disco, games, karaoke and competitions) for £60. Suitable for 5-12 years. Food and drink £3.50 per head or, for £20 charge you can provide your own.

Springfield Leisure Centre
✉ Beechfield Road, Corsham, Wiltshire
☎ 01249 712846
Club room with kitchenette available for 2 hours with choice of 4 different 1 hour activities. Trampolining £37 for maximum of 12 children, pool party £41 for up to 25 children, £46 for maximum of 50, bouncy castle party £34, maximum 25 children, mixed games party £24 with up to 20 children (optional recreational assistant £5), soft play party £25 maximum 25 children. Parents provide food.

Wellow Trekking Centre
✉ Little Horse Croft Farm, Wellow
☎ 834376
For over 3s a half hour pony ride, £5 per child. For over 6s an hour's ride, £9 per child. Riding hats provided. Children's play area, picnic and barbecue areas. Bring your own picnic or pay extra for a barbecue.

Windmill Hill City Farm
✉ 33a Doveton Street, off St Philip Street, Bedminster, Bristol
☎ 0117 9633252
Look around the farm (plenty of animals), an hour of fun in the rumpus room (under 8s only), and 45 minutes in the play centre for food and games. Café food at reasonable prices or take your own. Closed Monday. Open other days 9am-dusk.

Yate Leisure Centre
✉ Yate ☎ 01454 310111
2 soft playrooms for hire: over 5s or under 5s. £19.10 per hour, maximum of 20 children. Very popular at weekends, so book early. Trampoline and football parties available, also £19.10 per hour. For £25.75 you can hire the small pool for a swimming party. Will cater for Birthday tea if required.

Bath with your Kids 55

Entertainment and Entertainers

Children's Party Entertainers

Bath Puppet Theatre
☎ 312173
Can be booked for private parties in your own home for £70.

Boggle
☎ 446685
Offer a full range of children's entertainers: jugglers, clowns, magicians, balloon modellers, face painters, all tailored to individual needs.

Bryan the Magician
☎ 427274
Professional entertainer who can run party for you if required. Balloon modelling, puppets, games, magic and competitions with lots of audience participation. Can also provide filled party bags, balloons and novelties.

Cookie the Clown
☎ 01380 813658
For children 3 years and over, Cookie will clown about or run the party for you. Includes games, magic, sweets and a sack of surprises. Top rates. Book early as very popular.

Funny Faces
☎ 0117 9864740/0117 9863243
Professional artist, lovely results. Minimum 10 children, £2 per child. No petrol charge if party is in local area.

Ghost Walks
☎ 463618
Pre-booked children's tours of ghostly haunts of Bath, starting outside the Garrick's Head (next to Theatre Royal). From 6:30pm lasting up to two hours. Suitable for children over 6 years. £20 for ten children plus two adults.

Instant Music
☎ 0117 558867
An hour's entertainment: music games, instrument making, singing etc. £40 plus travel expenses.

Jack Stephens
☎ 01380 850453
All-round entertainer: balloon modelling, magic, puppets, guitar, singing and games. 45 minutes entertainment (no games) or will run the whole party for 2 hours. Suitable for 3-8 years.

John Issacs and Mr. Marvo
☎ 873945
Thoroughly entertaining and accomplished magician with plenty of young audience participation. Magic balloon modelling and live rabbit. Brings along human rabbit, Mr. Marvo, only for school fetes, fundays etc.

Magical Mandy
☎ 429876
45 minutes magic show or half hour of games and half hour of magic. Entertaining magician who can provide prizes for all children and a balloon animal.

Peter Stedman
☎ 01249 813478
Professional entertainer who will run your party and include magic, Punch and Judy, balloon modelling, paper folding, or games.

Bryan the Magician
Magical Entertainment
provided for

CHILDREN'S PARTIES : SCHOOLS
CONCERTS : CLUBS : FETES
FAMILY DAYS : CORPORATE EVENTS
New Programmes arranged for Repeat Engagements

CHILDREN'S ENTERTAINMENT A SPECIALITY

PUPPETS : BALLOON ANIMALS
GAMES ORGANISED : COMPETITIONS
AUDIENCE PARTICIPATION
COMPLETE PARTIES ARRANGED

GAS FILLED BALLOONS
FLOATING BALLOON ARCHES

FILLED PARTY BAGS : BALLOONS
NOVELTIES
RING BATH 01225 427274
7, Longfellow Ave, Bath BA2 4SJ (no Callers)

Entertainment and Entertainers

Roy Grout
☎ 810064
Professional children's entertainer with 30 years experience. Magic, live rabbit, doves, Punch and Judy and games if required.

Simple Simon
☎ 313551
One hour magic show for birthday parties catering for children from 3-12 years.

Wastenot Workshops
☎ 0117 550847
Craft activities, using materials from Scrap Store. Children create hobby horses, kites, masks etc. to take home. Also face painting, badge making, dressing up, parachute games. £50 an hour plus 30p per mile.

Zilly the Clown
☎ 766496
1 hour show of magic and balloon fun with plenty of children's participation. Can provide face painters. Suitable for 3-12 years.

EQUIPMENT HIRE – BOUNCY CASTLES ETC.

Useful if you are organising fetes or other fund raising events.

ABC Inflatables
☎ 01373 830818
Hire ballponds and bouncy castles from £30.

Boomerang
☎ 702000
Several different bouncy castles for hire.

Bouncers
☎ 01761 436328
Variety of equipment including bouncy castles, Quad bikes, Barfly and Gladiators.
Also individually designed birthday cakes. A supervisor always stays with larger pieces of equipment.

John Dench
☎ 872908
Swing boats for hire.
Also a smashing train available for fetes and fund raising events.

Huxham Leisure
☎ 753553
Ball ponds and bouncy castles for hire. Also barbecues, crockery, cutlery, tables and chairs.

Jolly Jumpers Amusement Hire
☎ 01373 453053
40 inflatables, ball pools, velcro fly traps, inflatable marquees for hire. Also a variety of fete equipment: coconut shies, cork rifles, pick-a-key, tombola, hoopla etc.

Jeff Rodway
☎ 01633 871427
Model ride along train for fetes, events etc.

THEATRES

Bath Unity Players
☎ 334358
Perform a traditional family pantomime, usually with dancers from Dorothy Coleborn School of Dancing. Held at Kingswood School, lots of audience participation.

Professional children's entertainment for your next party

Magic with live rabbit! Doves!

Punch and Judy!

Presented by Magic Circle member

Roy Grout
12 Highlands Close
Rudloe, Corsham
Wilts. SN13 0LA
Bath (01225) 810064

Entertainment and Entertainers

Bristol Old Vic Theatre Royal
✉ King Street, Bristol ☎ 0117 9877877
Saturday morning children's shows 11-12am £2 pay at the door. Mostly suitable for 4-11years. Pantomime, otherwise rarely stages plays suitable for children. Mailing list.

Bristol Hippodrome
✉ St. Augustines Parade, Bristol
☎ 0117 299444
Often stage shows for children: Postman Pat, Fireman Sam, Roald Dahl adaptations, ballet, Christmas pantomime. NCP car park 5 minutes walk. Postal or phone bookings. Mailing list.

Merlin Theatre and Arts Centre
✉ Bath Road, Frome ☎ 01373 465949
Community theatre offering wide variety of amateur and professional productions. Reasonable prices. Frequent family performances including puppets, children's classics, music and dance. Free mailing list. Well signposted. Free parking. Saturday Club for 7-11years – see **Activities and Clubs**, *Drama*.

Rondo
✉ St. Saviours Road, Larkhall, Bath
☎ 332579
Venue for both amateur and professional productions with varying programme. Well equipped, intimate (104 seats). Available for hire for meetings etc. Mailing list. Sometimes stages a pantomime in January.

St. Barnabas Players
☎ 334358
Perform a traditional family panto. Well-aimed at younger children. Usually staged at Culverhay Boys' School, Rush Hill. Tickets on sale from beginning November.

Theatre Royal
✉ Sawclose, Bath
☎ 448844
Join their free mailing list for regular information. Occasionally have shows for children. Pantomime usually runs from December-January. You can book by phone using credit card (448861 but this can be time-consuming) or by post or in person. Standby seats are available from 10am on day of performance. Youth group - see **Activities and Clubs**, *Drama*.

CINEMAS

Cannon Cinema
✉ Westgate Street
☎ 462959
May get PG or U certificate films on their circuit. Check local press for details. Matinees every day.

Little Theatre
✉ St. Michaels Place
☎ 466822
Rarely shows children's films. Matinees at weekends only.

Robin's
✉ St. John's Place
☎ 461506/481465
On the Disney circuit. Junior film club for children 5-12 years, Saturday 2-4pm, during term time. Children entertained until 4pm if film is less than 2 hours. Competitions, puzzles, Christmas party. Annual membership £2.50, weekly cost £1.25 (members) £2.00 (non-members).

Fun For Free!

Here's a few ideas for free fun! You may find it useful to refer to the Trips and Jaunts and Parks chapters for more details. Once you've tried our suggestions, you'll probably think of loads more...

Outdoors

Duck feeding spots in Bath

Behind Horseshoe Walk – canal pools
Pulteney Weir
Sydney Gardens – canal
Victoria Park

Duck feeding spots out of Bath

Biddestone pond
Bradford-on-Avon canal
Bradford-on-Avon river
Saltford – Jolly Sailors Riverside
Wells – moat around Bishops Palace

Kite Flying spots in Bath

Hills above Weston Rec.
Lansdown playing Fields (Bath & North East Somerset ones)
Mount Road Park
Rosewarn Close Adventure Playground
Solsbury Hill
Springfield Farm Park

Other Outdoor Activities

Abbey Churchyard and other busking spots
Avon Valley Railway, Bitton
Balloon take-offs
Bands in parks
Bradford-on-Avon Country Park
Cycle track, Bath to Bitton
Kennet and Avon Canal – lock watching
Markets and cattle markets
National Trust – free day in spring
Parade Gardens (free for residents)
Parks' children's entertainment
Train and plane spotting
Westbury White Horse

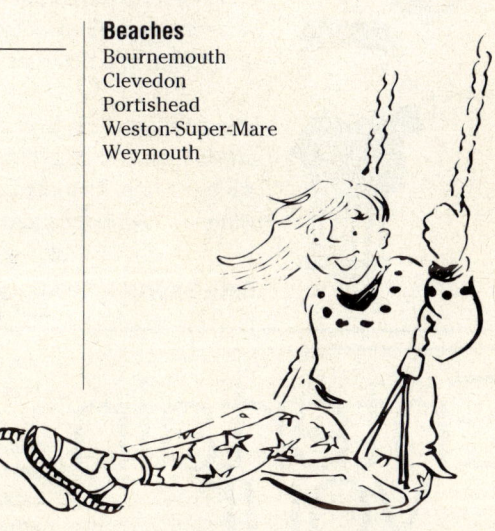

Beaches

Bournemouth
Clevedon
Portishead
Weston-Super-Mare
Weymouth

Indoors

Bath & North East Somerset residents only

Bath Open Week – free admission to museums. Usually autumn half-term.
Bath Postal Museum
Museum of Costume
Roman Baths

Free for all

Assembly Rooms
Bath Abbey (donation requested)
Libraries
Victoria Art Gallery

Balance, co-ordination and fun for toddlers

A series of exciting and entertaining courses for children of three months to four years old. Activities include exercises, songs, use of various apparatus, and activities in the new leisure pool.

The sessions help to encourage your children to gain confidence and co-ordination in safe and enjoyable surroundings. The instructors are fully qualified. Ring the centre for more details.

Bath Sports & Leisure Centre 01225-462563/5

Entertain your family
FOR JUST £1.70!

Every fortnight, Venue magazine brings you hundreds of ideas for things to do and places to go. The comprehensive listings sections cover everything from the latest cinema releases to events and exhibitions and now, in the new look Venue, there is a Family section in addition to the popular Kids page.

So if you want to get out with the family this year, get Venue magazine at your newsagent every fortnight just £1.70

SPECIAL SUBSCRIPTION OFFER!
A years subscription for just £35.00 (only £1.35 per issue)
Simply call 0117 942 8491 and ask for Subscriptions, alternatively send a cheque for £35.00 made payable to Greetlake Services Ltd to:
Venue Publishing, 64-65 North Road, St.Andrews, Bristol, BS6 5AQ.

Venue MAGAZINE

Green Issues for Families

Many parents find that starting a family is a time when they begin to consider the impact that they and their offspring have on the environment. All those nappies to deal with and healthy meals to cook may get you thinking seriously about how to make your family greener. If you are a full-time parent you may have more time but much less money to budget with, so energy efficiency and increased self-sufficiency make perfect sense during this stage in your life.

Bath is very well-blessed with schemes and shops to help you select the aspects of a green lifestyle most appropriate for your family. Here are some suggestions of where to start.

Bath City Farm

✉ Kelston View
☎ Project coordinator - Paul Stephens 01761 432534 Planned to open fully in 1999.
Local group is seeking to create a city farm. Recent family days with hedge-laying and hedgerow maintenance. School-age children can use the project via their schools, otherwise contact Paul Stephens.

Bath Environment Centre

✉ 24 Milsom Street
☎ 460620
Open Tuesday-Saturday 10am-5pm. Voluntary organisation - green parents please apply! Meeting place for many groups. Information centre - books, videos and publications on a wide range of environmental matters. Atrium display of air-cleansing plants plus regularly-changing exhibitions. Children's corner. Good links with schools for kids events for example: kitemaking, community mapmaking for school-age children during holidays.

Bath LETS

☎ Peter Andrews 319117
LETS (Local Exchange Trading System) no-cost method of exchanging goods and services within a community eg. you need a babysitter and in return you offer to garden for someone else within scheme, building up credits and debits. A member directory listing all services offered is published - there are about 300 people involved in Bath, with meetings and training sessions held.

Global Action Plan UK

✉ Third Floor, 42 Kingsway,
London WC2B 6EX
☎ 0171 405 5633
Operates 3 programmes to help people take DIY environmental action. Meetings at Bath Environment Centre. Contact Deborah Morris, BANES Environmental Promotions Officer on 477662.

ORGANIC FOOD SUPPLIES

The Better Food Company

✉ Tim Baines
☎ 312116

Organic vegetables, fruit, and other good food available to order or as a seasonal selection box - a far wider range than any supermarket could offer.

Bath with your Kids 61

Green Issues for Families

Norwood Farm
- Norton St. Philip
- ☎ 01373 834356

Organic meat straight from the supplier - see **Trips and Jaunts** for further information.

Radford Mill Farm
- ☎ 01761 472541

Locally grown and imported produce. Phone for details of nearest Bath outlet, or visit the farm. Open days held to help families learn more about organic farming.

The Real Meat Company
- 6/7 Hayes Place, Bear Flat
- ☎ 335139

Organic and free range meat and poultry - specialist butcher skills so anything available to order. Also sells free range eggs, dairy produce, wholefoods, pickles and sauces etc.

Riverford Farm
- Buckfastleigh, Devon
- ☎ Libby Tiffin 01453 882856

Small, medium or large boxes of fresh organic produce delivered to your door.

ORGANIC GARDENING

Bath Environment Centre
(See full listing above.) Useful library of books. Help to coordinate English Apple Day at Parade Gardens, October (see **Annual Events**).

Bath Organic Group (BOG)
- 37 Paragon, Bath
- ☎ Lucy Davis 463712

Workshops and meetings. Maintains organic demo. garden at Lower Common, Royal Victoria Park, open to public at certain times.

Bath Permaculture Group
- ☎ Peter Andrews 319117

Chase Organics
- ☎ 01932 820958

Well thought-of Organic Gardening Catalogue – excellent for seeds, books, equipment, etc

Henry Doubleday Research Association (HDRA)
- Ryton Organic Gardens, Ryton-on-Dunsmore, Coventry CV8 3LG
- ☎ 01203 303517

Ten acres of demonstration gardens plus good children's area. Shop and restaurant serving organic produce. Publications, courses and workshops, Heritage Seed Library to save old, unusual and outlawed vegetables and increase biodiversity.

RECYCLING

BANES Recycling Dept
- ☎ 477000 ext. 7124

Phone to be included in weekly Green Box kerbside collections from outside your home. You get a green box and information. Also publish useful leaflets on recycling issues and information. Available on the number above and at the library.

The Civic Amenity Site
- off Midland Bridge Road, opposite Royal Victoria Park adventure playground. To dump rubbish that the Council won't remove.

REUSABLE NAPPIES

Firstborn
- 32 Bloomfield Avenue, Bath BA2 3AB
- ☎ Deb Steele 422586

Washable Danish-style cloth nappies in cotton muslin, with woollen Wunderpants (knitted outerpants made from specially treated wool) to hold the washables in place.

The Green Store
- Green Street, Bath ☎ 427155

Information and advice on reusable nappies which can be machine-washed and tumble-dried. Two systems on sale.

The Real Nappy Association
- PO Box 3704 London SE26 4RX

Parent's information and pressure group aims to be source of advice on all nappy-related issues. Membership fee, newsletters and Real Nappy Hotline for members enquiries. (See **Mail Order** for environmentally friendly products for parents by post.)

Health Care

This chapter outlines the main health professionals and organisations relevant to families with young children - additional information on specific support groups may also be found in the Advice and Support section of this book. Bath and West Community NHS Trust provides most of the Bath area with family health services. You can contact them on 313640.

NHS FAMILY MEDICINE

Primary Health Care Team consists of your family doctor(GP), community midwife, health visitor, district nurse, practice nurse, social worker and community psychiatric nurse.

Family Doctor (GP)

It is advisable to register with a GP – newborn babies not automatically registered, it is your responsibility. Names and addresses of Doctors listed in Yellow Pages under Doctors - Medical Practitioners also available from public libraries.

Community Midwife

Usually based at local clinic or health centre. She/he will share in your care during pregnancy and advise you of the choices available to you. Post-natal visits are made to your home for up to ten days after your baby's birth to advise on feeding, care of the baby and post-natal nursing. For those having a domino delivery or home birth, she/he may also deliver your baby.

Health Visitor

Health Visitors are Registered General Nurses with midwifery experience, and further training in child development, health education and the social aspects of health. They are notified about all births in their area and it is their professional duty to visit each mother and baby 15 days after birth. Contact with children continues at local clinics and by home visits until the child is attending full-time education. Health Visitors can advise on all aspects of your child's development.

Family Planning

Available free of charge from most GPs and health authority clinics, listed in the Yellow Pages under Family Planning. You can choose where you go for care and advice. Emergency contraception, confidential pregnancy testing and testing for sexually transmitted diseases are available from:

Brook Advisory Centre
✉ 25 Denmark Street, Bristol BS1 5DQ
☎ 0117 929 0090.

HEALTH CARE FOR PREGNANCY

Folic Acid

The Department of Health advises women planning a pregnancy to take a 400mcg (0.4mg) tablet of folic acid every day before she gets pregnant and until the 12th week of her pregnancy. Proven to reduce the risk of spina bifida. Tablets available from most chemists and GP's. Leaflets on how to include folic acid-rich foods into your diet should be available from your surgery.

Pregnancy Tests

For a reliable test it is usually best to wait at least 2 weeks after the first day of a missed period. Take a sample of early morning urine in a clean bottle, clearly labelled with your name and the date of your last period. Tests are available from your GP, Family Planning Clinic, most chemists (for a fee) and from the following:

Brook Advisory Centre
☎ 0117 929 0090

Bath with your Kids 63

Health Care

British Pregnancy Advisory Service
☎ 873321 (24 hour answering service). Charitable trust offering counselling and treatment on all aspects of pregnancy and termination. Also on female sterilisation, vasectomy and reversal of both of these.

Antenatal Care
Once you know that you are pregnant contact your GP as soon as possible so arrangements can be made for your care and the birth. You may transfer to another doctor (if for instance, you want a home birth and your own GP is unsympathetic to your wishes). If this is the case, get a letter from your GP or Health Visitor.

A Certificate of Pregnancy will be given to you on booking with midwife (8-10 weeks), this entitles you to free prescriptions and dental care until one year after the birth. A Certificate of Expected Confinement given at 26 weeks enables you to claim Statutory Maternity Pay, Maternity Allowance or other DSS payments. If you are working, the 1994 Employment Act gives you the right to take time off for antenatal care. Ask your employer for information about maternity pay, eligibility to change your work conditions during pregnancy and your right to return to work after maternity leave. Additional support and information from:

Association For Improvements in Maternity Services
✉ 40 Kingswood Avenue, London NW6 6LS
☎ 0181 960 5585

Independent Midwives Association
☎ 0181 406 3172
Registered midwives operating independently from GP's.

Maternity Alliance
✉ 15 Brittania Street, London WC1X 9JP
☎ 0171 837 1265
Information on maternity rights and benefits.

Maternity Links
✉ The Old Co-op, 42 Chelsea Road, Bristol BS5 6AF
Interpretation and advocacy service for pregnant women whose first language is not English.

Antenatal/Parentcraft Classes
Aim to give you information and confidence about becoming a parent. An excellent way to meet other first time parents. Find out about labour and the birth, changes to your body, exercises, relaxation techniques, pain relief and how to care for and feed baby. **NHS** classes are run by midwives, health visitors and obstetric physiotherapists, at clinics, health centres or the hospital. Ask when you attend antenatal appointments for a tour of the hospital of your choice. **NCT** (National Childbirth Trust) antenatal evening classes are for pregnant women and birth partners. Aim to inform parents about choices available during pregnancy and early parenthood and to enable them to face their baby's birth with confidence. Fee may be waived for those not in full time employment. Book a place at about 12-15 weeks because courses are often full (telephone number from Community Midwife). Antenatal Yoga and Relaxation Classes in Fairfield Park, Bath. Full details from your Community Midwife.

AFTER YOUR BABY IS BORN

Registration of births
✉ 12 Charlotte Street ☎ 312032
The birth or stillbirth of your baby must be registered by one of the parents within 42 days by the Registrar of the district in which the child is born. If parents are not married, both must attend to get their joint names on the register. A short certificate giving name, sex, date of birth and place of birth is issued free at the time of registration. A full birth certificate, with names and occupations of both parents is available for a small fee.

Association of Breastfeeding Mothers
✉ PO Box 411, St. Alban's, Herts. AL4 OAS
☎ 0181 778 4769
☎ Local telephone counsellor:
Helen Sheppard 0117 966 1788
Counselling services by volunteer mothers. Local meetings – opportunities to meet other mothers and babies.

Home Support Service
Maternity Home Care can sometimes be provided during the baby's first two weeks.

64 Bath with your Kids

Health Care

Ask your midwife, doctor, health visitor or social worker for assistance if you think you will need extra help at home eg. if you are expecting twins or triplets and have no relatives to help with other siblings. A fee may be charged according to income.

La Leche League
✉ BM 2434, London WC1N 3XX
☎ 0171 242 1278
Information and support, through personal contact, to women who want to breastfeed. National switchboard, (Monday-Friday 9am-6pm) lists local counsellors and details of meetings.

National Childbirth Trust
✉ Alexandra House, Oldham Terrace, London W3 6NH
☎ 0181 992 8637

NCT Bath and District Branch
✉ Irene Arnold, Membership Secretary
7 Harding Place, Keynsham, Bristol
☎ 0117 986 6360
Charity staffed by local volunteer mothers offering post natal support. Open Houses: meet other parents at their homes. Local three-times-a-year newsletter details all activities and services. Nearly New clothing and equipment sales and the local agents for MAVA feeding bras and Egnell Breast Pump Hire. An experiences register is kept which can put you in touch with families who may have experienced a similar pregnancy or health concern to your own.

NCT Breastfeeding Counsellors
☎ Cath McCombe 317997
NCT breastfeeding counsellors are all mothers who have breastfed their babies. They know how worthwhile and enjoyable breastfeeding can be, but are also aware of how to offer help and support that many breastfeeding mothers need. Can provide information and emotional support. Free service to anyone.

Postnatal Classes
Group sessions at GPs surgeries or Health Centres for mums and babies about six weeks after the birth. Good time to meet other new mothers and wide range of useful topics is covered. Ask your Health Visitor.

Postnatal Exercise Classes
Get back into shape and meet other mothers for a cuppa and chat while wonderful WI volunteers keep an eye on your (hopefully) sleeping babes. Free. Manvers Street Baptist Church weekly. See **Sanctuaries for Adults**.

YOUR CHILD'S HEALTH

Child Health Clinics
Your GP's clinic or Health Centre may offer a programme for monitoring the development of your child up to 5 years. Regular height, weight, growth checks and develop-mental assessments. Full range of immunisations against childhood illnesses will be offered – parents choose whether or not to have their children immunised. Discuss any concerns

Health Care

about immunisation with your GP or Health Visitor or telephone the immunisation hotline at the Royal United Hospital, Bath ☎ 313640 ext 340. (See **Advice and Support** for self-help groups).

Dental Care

Dentists are listed in the Yellow Pages under Dental Surgeons. Not all Bath dentists accept new NHS patients – ask other parents for a recommendation if you find trouble in registering. Dental care is free for children, for pregnant women and mothers up to one year after the birth of their baby.

Eye Care

GPs and Health Visitors check eyes at 9 and 18 months and check for visual acuity at three and a half years (pre-school test). In case of problems your child may be referred to an ophthalmic optician in a hospital clinic. Opticians are listed in the Yellow Pages. Children are eligible for a free annual eye examination between the ages of 1 and 16.

For Emergencies

Royal United Hospital Casualty Department
☎ 428331
Will give telephone advice if for instance, your child has fallen, been burnt, cut themselves or consumed something they shouldn't have. If you have no transport of your own and need to get your child to hospital quickly, call an Ambulance on 999.

If your Child Needs Hospital Treatment

Action For Sick Children (NAWCH Ltd.)
✉ 32, Combe Park, Bath
☎ 421480
Provides an information and counselling service for parents whose child is sick or receiving hospital treatment.

Pharmacies and Local Chemists

Qualified pharmacists can give useful advice on a range of drugs, creams and other remedies. They may be available when your clinic or doctor is not. At least one pharmacy in Bath will open for limited out of hours dispensing in evenings and Sundays. Evening Chronicle publishes details and your doctor's surgery should have this information too.

COMPLEMENTARY MEDICINE

Many alternatives to NHS health care are now widely available. We aim to provide enough information for you to find your chosen therapy locally.

This section is not intended as an endorsement of a particular treatment or any individual practitioner.

Acupuncture

✉ Directory of British Acupuncturists, The Council For Acupuncture, 179, Gloucester Place, London NW1 6DX
☎ 0171 724 5756
✉ The British Medical Acupuncture Society, Newton House, Newton Lane, Whitley, Warrington, Cheshire WA4 4JA
Traditional Chinese therapy where fine needles are inserted at points in the body. Anyone may set up an acupuncture practice - check that therapist is a registered practitioner.

Alexander Technique

✉ The Society of Teachers of the
Alexander Technique,
10 London House, 266 Fulham Road, London SW10 9EL
☎ 0171 352 0666
Aims to help person attain ideal, natural posture. Can be useful for back pain. Technique taught individually or in group sessions. Lots of practical hands-on support.

Aromatherapy

International Federation of Aromatherapists
☎ 0181 846 8066
Concentrated essences or essential oils distilled from plants thought to have medicinal properties, used mostly for external massage. Phone for list of local therapists.

Bach Flower Remedies

✉ The Dr E Bach Centre,
Mount Vernon, Wallingford, Oxon OX10 OPZ
☎ 01491 834678
38 preparations made from the flowers of wild plants said to have properties to treat the whole person.

Health Care

Chiropractice

✉ The British Chiropractic Association
Equity House, 29 Whitley Street,
Reading, Berks. RG2 OEG
☎ 01734 757557
Work with the structural relationship between nerve tissues and spinal column. Aim to correct disorders of joints (particularly spine) that may be caused by childhood accident or childbirth. Check practitioner is fully qualified.

Cranial Osteopathy

✉ The Cranial Osteopathic Association,
478 Baker Street, Enfield, Middlesex EN1 3QS
☎ 0181 367 5561
Delicate manipulation of skull and facial bones. List of practitioners from above address.

Homeopathy

✉ British Homeopathic Association,
27a Devonshire Street, London W1N 1RJ
☎ 0171 935 2163
Remedies which aim to stimulate body's natural healing resources. Send large SAE for addresses of Homeopathic doctors and pharmacies.

Medical Herbalism

✉ The National Institute of Medical Herbalists
56 Longbrook Street, Exeter EX4 6AH
☎ 01392 426022
Practitioners are trained in same diagnostic skills as orthodox doctors, but take a more holistic approach to illness. Plant remedies to restore the body's natural balance and mobilise its own healing rather than treating symptoms of illness in isolation.

Osteopathy

✉ General Council and Register of Osteopaths
56 London Street, Reading, Berks RG1 4SQ
☎ 01734 576585
Diagnosis and treatment of mechanical problems in the framework of the body, may be caused by injury or stress. Osteopaths use their hands for massaging and manipulating the body in order to restore comfortable posture. Send for a list of registered osteopaths.

Reflexology

✉ Holistic Association of Reflexologists/
British School of Reflexology
☎ 01279 429060

Reflexologists massage what they call reflex points on the feet which correspond to the major organs, glands and body parts. Believed to stimulate the body to heal itself.

Shiatsu

✉ The Shiatsu Society
5 Foxcote, Wokingham, Berks RG11 3PG
☎ 01734 730836
Based on same principle as acupuncture, but the practitioner uses fingers, palms, elbows, knees and feet to apply pressure to the body. Information about shiatsu in pregnancy and childbirth and list of registered practitioners are available.

COMPLEMENTARY THERAPIES IN BATH

Bath Health Group

✉ The Secretary,
57 Queen's Drive, Bath BA2 5PB
Send an SAE plus 29p in stamps for information on the many therapies available in Bath plus an annually updated directory of practitioners. Not fully comprehensive but a good starting place. Gives a good checklist of questions to ask your chosen practitioner.

Bath Centre For Counselling and Psychotherapy

✉ 1 Walcot Terrace, London Road,
Bath BA1 6AB
☎ 466635/833657
A referral service. All BCPC members work within an agreed code of ethics.

Bath Clinic of Traditional Acupuncture/Bath Natural Health Centre

✉ 7 Laura Place
☎ 466271

Bath Natural Health Clinic

✉ Alexander House, James Street West,
Bath BA1 2BP
☎ 313153
A number of different therapies including cranial osteopathy, reflexology, shiatsu, chiropractic, medical herbalism and massage therapy.

Health Care

Centre For Complementary Medicine
✉ Newbridge Surgery,
129 Newbridge Hill, Bath
☎ 337836
A group of complementary practitioners specialising in acupuncture, environmental medicine and homeopathy, massage and stress management, osteopathy and physiotherapy. Hold open days when free demonstrations are given and you can talk informally to practitioners.

The Chinese Medical Centre
✉ Manvers Chambers, Manvers Street, Bath BA1 1PE
☎ 483393
Chinese medical practitioners trained in both Western and traditional Chinese medicine. Therapies include chinese herbal treatments, acupuncture, moxibustion, massage and herbal creams.

Green Treats
✉ 2b Burton Street, Bath BA1 1BN
☎ 446332
Formerly offering mainly massage and beauty treatments, this pleasant non-medical first floor treatment centre above the Body Shop now provides working space for a wide range of alternative practitioners including a homeopath, medical herbalist, aromatherapist, reflexologist and a specialist in baby massage.

The Key Centre For Complementary Therapies
✉ 2 North Parade Passage, Bath BA1 1NX
☎ 420953 (24 hour answerphone)
Acupuncture, allergy testing, aromatherapy, the Feldenkrais method, healing, homeopathy, shiatsu, massage, nutritional advice, osteopathy and psychotherapy.

Openings Centre For Personal Growth, Counselling and Psychotherapy
✉ Bluecoat House, Sawclose, Bath BA1 1EY
☎ 445013 (24 hour answerphone)
All practitioners represented by this centre are required to share the same code of ethics. There is a range of experience from those in the final stages of their training through to therapists with ten years or more experience. Bookings made through administrator who can supply information list on the practitioners represented.

The Polden Naturopathic Service
✉ 1 The Orchard, Corston near Bath BA2 9AA
Send SAE to Mrs Alison Edwards, Practice Manager for information on elimination diets and the Bicom magnetic treatment. Used in the treatment of complaints such as asthma, migraine, arthritis and food allergies.

Stillpoint
✉ Broad Street Place, Broad Street ☎ 460106
Used by a number of complementary therapists including a homeopathist and a cranial osteopathist.

Libraries – Books and Toys

BOOK LIBRARIES

Bath Central Library
✉ The Podium, Northgate Street
☎ 428144

Separate area for children, with train displaying picture books for under 5's, separate sections for different age groups, and a large non-fiction area. There are children's librarians available for information and advice. There is no lower age limit for joining, and child members may borrow up to four books or tapes for four weeks. Special tickets are available for toddler groups, and playgroups enabling them to borrow a greater number of books.

The library offers a variety of activity workshops in the holidays (book in advance) and they hold weekly storytelling sessions, where parents may leave their child while they browse in the library themselves - but must not leave the building. Children listen to stories, followed by a related activity, like drawing or colouring.

- Under-5's storytime:
Tuesday 2.15-2.45pm
- Over-4's storytime:
Saturday 11-11.30am

Mobile Library
Provides a weekly service to the suburbs of the city. It carries a stock of books and story tapes for all ages. For times and places, enquire at the Central Library.

Moorland Road Branch Library
☎ 424357

Books, tapes and jigsaws. Storytime: Second Thursday in the month 2.15-2.45pm. Access for buggies very difficult.

TOY LIBRARIES

Toy libraries are open to all under 5's and those with special needs. They are also open to any one who cares for children including children's groups, health visitors and other specialists. A small annual membership fee is charged for which you are able to borrow 3-4 toys for a period of 3 weeks. Groups pay a slightly higher fee but are able to borrow up to 10 toys for 4 weeks. Both groups in Bath are members of the National Toy Libraries Association. Children can try out toys before choosing which to take home and parents can enjoy a chat and a cup of coffee! The libraries understand that losses and breakages will sometimes occur, and

Libraries

simply ask that you take reasonable care of the toys that you borrow. They often need help, so if you have just half an hour to give, this can be an enjoyable way of ensuring they continue to thrive.

Toybox Toy Library

✉ Hillside Hall, Hillside Road, Oldfield Park
☎ 337177
Open Friday 10am-11.30. Run by local parents of pre-school children.

WRVS Bath Toy Library

✉ Riverside Youth Centre, London Road. (opposite Shell garage, and behind Porterbutt pub) ☎ 837997 Open Thursday 10am-12noon.

STAR Multicultural Resource Library

✉ 7 Barton Buildings ☎ 334415
This library contains books, toys, dolls, puzzles, dressing-up clothes, puppets, musical instruments, tapes etc. from many different cultures. Ideas for ways of using the resources are included. The boxes are available for loan to toddler groups, playgroups, nurseries and individual carers, on payment of an annual registration fee. Open Friday 1-2pm, term time only.

SUPPORT TRAINING AND RESOURCES

STAR (Support and Training Against Racism)

✉ 7 Barton Buildings ☎ 334415
STAR offers support, training and resources enabling adults to provide for racial equality in the care and education of young children. The training explores why we need to take into account differences of racial origin, religion, language and cultural background. It examines how we can treat children with equal respect and concern and encourage these positive attitudes in all children.
Also has many books, leaflets and videos are available for loan. Also run a Multicultural Resource Library - see above under *Toy Libraries*.

Bath Community Bus

☎ 465125
Bath Community Bus is a mobile resource covering Bath and North East Somerset in areas that lack community facilities. It reaches people who are socially or geographically isolated. The Bus is a double-decker, kitted out for play activities, but can be used for a variety of purposes including training and crafts for adults.
The workers on the Bus help people to set up their own groups, for instance parent and toddlers. The project responds to the changing needs of the area by visiting different sites on a regular weekly session basis.

Scrapstore

✉ Queen Quay, Welshback, Bristol BS1 4SL
☎ 0117 9252229
A wonderful treasure house of office, industrial and household surplus material offering great scope for art, craft and play. Groups can join and pay an annual fee, enabling them to purchase in bulk and at low cost. Membership is not open to individuals. Scrapstore also hires out play equipment, for example, badge makers and musical instruments.

BATH HARDWOOD FLOORS

Hardwood floors from sustainable sources supplied and fitted

WOODEN FLOORS SANDED
STAINED AND SEALED

FREE ESTIMATES

01225 427478

Loo Stops

Public Toilets are open 7.30am-6.30pm in winter, 7.00am-9.30pm in summer. They are opened and closed in rotation, so times are approximate. Many have been refurbished or rebuilt over the last ten years to provide 'anti-vandal' facilities which are basic and mostly very cold! It is difficult for fathers to gain access to most baby rooms – obviously the message is not getting through. Full marks to Marks and Spencer whose toilets have baby changing facilities in both the Women's and the Men's.

SEE MAP ON PAGES 136/7

1. Charlotte Street Car Park
▣ Off Charlotte Street. Small block with 3 basic but clean loos just outside car park. Easy access for pushchairs, but no changing or feeding facilities. Disabled facilities (RADAR).

2. Claverton Street
▣ Just before Lyncombe Hill and crossing. Basic but clean.

3. Ham Gardens
▣ Off Henry Street, near freezer centre. 24 HOURS. Mother and baby room in ladies, extensive facilities (hurrah!) If locked, key with attendant (8.30am-4.30pm). Ample loos, room for numerous buggies, toddlers, mothers, nannies, grannies... Good double and single pushchair access. Disabled facilities (RADAR).

4. Henrietta Park
▣ Henrietta Street (off Great Pulteney Street) Toilet block with two stainless steel loos. No changing or feeding facilities at all. Good pushchair access. Disabled facilities (RADAR).

5. Lansdown Road
▣ At the bottom of the hill. Basic but it's there in an emergency...

6. North Parade Road
▣ By Cricket ground. Basic, clean. No changing or disabled access.

7. Parade Gardens
▣ Grand Parade Toilets in a spectacular setting! Clean and spacious. Changing and feeding facilities may be locked, but key available from attendant at entrance kiosk from March-October. November-February, key available from attendant or gardener! Good access. Disabled (RADAR).

8. The Podium Shopping Centre
▣ Northgate Street (just outside Waitrose). Alas, no facilities for parents and babies. Room for buggies. Also loo inside Centre upstairs, but very cramped inside. Open all evening. Disabled facilities (RADAR) in both loos.

9. Riverside Coach Park
▣ Avon Street. Lovely loo block, very clean. BUT mother and baby room only accessible with key, obtainable from an attendant in the same block from 8am-5pm, Easter to September - then what??

10. Royal Victoria Park
▣ Children's Play Area. Separate loos for children and adults with child-only access inside the play area. Attendant available. Roomy, easy access for pushchairs. Feeding possible, But there's no specific changing area. No facilities in men's loos either - just do your best! Disabled facilities (RADAR).

11. Royal Victoria Park
▣ Royal Avenue (near Tennis Courts). New modern block with basic 'Wallgate' facilities. Clean and well maintained. Mother and baby room with good access.

12. Royal Victoria Park
▣ Weston Road (near Golf Course) Easy access, but no changing or feeding facilities (sorry, golfers!) Disabled facilities (RADAR).

Loo Stops

13. Sandpits Play Area
▪ Monksdale Road, Oldfield Park. Two loo toilet block. Disabled facilities (RADAR).

14. Sawclose
▪ Opposite Theatre. Access with pushchairs OK. Changing and feeding facilities. Disabled facilities.

15. Seven Dials
▪ Monmouth Street. OPEN 24 HOURS. Baby changing room with low bench for changing or maybe sitting on to feed. Would be possible for Fathers to use this room. Disabled facilities.

16. Sydney Gardens
▪ By park entrance. No suitable place to change or feed a baby. Good pushchair access. Disabled facilities (RADAR).

Loos Open During Shop Hours

17. Adams
▪ Southgate. Excellent facilities, designed with children in mind. Child height and adult toilet. Also baby changing. Clean and well looked after. Single buggy ok, doubles will have to be left in shop.

18. Boots
▪ Southgate. Cosy, well-stocked baby-changing and feeding room. Not very much space. Available to Fathers. No Loo in store, apparently available on request, but Assistants take some persuading!

19. Early Learning Centre
▪ Cheap Street. Small but fully-equipped in-store 'mother and baby' room. Upstairs loo available on request.

20. Green Park Station
▪ Green Park Road. A public convenience in stunning architectural surroundings with changing facilities and feeding area. Pushchairs are best left outside.

21. Homebase
▪ Near Green Park Station. Clean loo in entrance area. Access is difficult for pushchairs – leave outside. Disabled facilities.

22. Jolly's
▪ Milsom Street. Small loo, accessible by lift. Pushchairs left outside in shop. Attendant. Anteroom for changing and feeding.

23. Littlewoods
▪ Stall Street. Spacious loos on first floor, lift access. Lots of doors! Clean changing and feeding area.

24. Marks and Spencer
▪ Stall Street. Spacious loos on the second floor, with lift access. Changing bench in both Ladies and Gents. Plenty of room for buggies, even doubles!

25. Mothercare
▪ Southgate. Feeding and changing room at back of shop with cubicles. Loo on request up numerous steps! (Usually direct you to Adams!) Available to fathers if no mothers object.

26. Pump Room
▪ Abbey Churchyard. Well-kept loos with small mother and baby room (cupboard)just inside Ladies. A bit cramped - buggies have to be left in corridor.

27. WH Smith
▪ Stall Street. Loo for disabled users on first floor. Lift. access.

28. Waterstones
▪ Milsom Street. Unfortunately, the loos are upstairs with no lift, changing or feeding facilities. BUT staff have haloes and are always helpful. Shop open later than some.

Supermarket Loos

29. Sainsburys
Staff loo available in emergencies only. If assistants argue about this, insist – we have been assured that this is management policy.

30. Waitrose
Staff have been very helpful with requests to use staff loos. Public loos just outside Waitrose in Northgate Street. No baby-changing facilities, though. Also loos in Podium at top of escalator.

72 Bath with your Kids

Mail Order

Shopping by post is a useful option for those who don't enjoy the hassle of the high street with their children or who find shops inaccessible. Many mail order firms have been set up and run by parents from home to offer innovative and well-designed products that you won't find in the shops so if you use them you'll be supporting a fellow family. Postage and packing can seem expensive, but when you consider the escalating cost of city centre parking plus placatory snacks for your loved ones, shopping from the calm of your armchair has to be a treat.

PREGNANCY NEEDS

MATERNITY CLOTHES AND PRODUCTS
Blooming Marvellous

✉ PO Box 12F, Chessington, Surrey
☎ 0181 391 4822 24 hour catalogue line
Bright, bold and flattering designs in cotton, lycra and polyester. Shirts specially designed for discreet breastfeeding.

Expressions Breastfeeding

✉ CMS House, Basford Lane, Leekbrook, Staffs ST13 7DT
☎ 01538 399541
☎ Advice line 01538 386650 (8.30am-5pm Monday-Friday).
Medela Maternity and Nursing Bras, also breast pumps, pads, breast milk freezer bags etc.

Formes

✉ 313 Brompton Road, London SW3
☎ 0171 584 33 37
Stylish French mix and match separates and business clothes.

Jo Jo

✉ 134 Lots Road, London SW10 ORJ
☎ 0171 351 4112
Trendy jersey and denim separates and sportswear for Mum, plus babywear up to 5 years and nursery equipment.

Mothernature

✉ Acorn House, Brixham Avenue, Cheadle Hulme, Cheshire SK8 6JG
☎ 0161 485 7359
Good range of maternity and nursing bras, difficult-to-find larger sizes. Breastfeeding accessories from breastpads to breast pumps.

NCT Maternity Sales

✉ (National Childbirth Trust) 239 Shawbridge Street, Glasgow G43 1QN
☎ 0141 636 0600
Maternity night dresses, swimwear, MAVA breastfeeding bras and underwear. Useful books and booklets relating to pregnancy, baby clothes and equipment. Profits to the NCT.

NATURAL REMEDIES FOR PREGNANCY
Essential Well Being

✉ PO Box 160, Wokingham, Berks RG40 3YX
☎ 01734 791737
Range of products using gentle essential oils for relaxation during pregnancy and labour plus baby products and baby massage lotions.

Herbline UK

☎ 01323 832858
Lines open Tuesday, Wednesday and Friday 9am-3pm. Will advise which herbal remedies are safe during pregnancy and lactation.

Mothernature

✉ Acorn House, Cheadle Hulme, Cheshire SK8 6JG
☎ 0161 485 7359
Aromatherapy and natural remedies for use in pregnancy and childbirth plus a selection of useful books and pamphlets.

Bath with your Kids

Mail Order

Neal's Yard Remedies
✉ 31 King Street, Manchester M2 6AA
☎ 0161 831 7875
Natural beauty products for mother and baby, plus alternative health books. Nearest branch is at 126,Whiteladies Road, Bristol, BS8 2RP
☎ 0117 946 6034.

BIRTH AIDS
Nature's Gate
✉ PO Box 371, Basingstoke, Hants RG24 8GD
☎ 01256 346060
Obstetric TENS hire service. A non-invasive, drug free method of pain relief for use during labour. Rental by post for parents who want the peace of mind of having their own machine at home in late pregnancy.

Primary Products
✉ 61 Park Lane, Thatcham, Newbury, Berks RG18 3BZ
☎ 01635 869853
V-shaped pillows which are useful for getting comfortable during pregnancy and also while breastfeeding. Often used in antenatal and relaxation classes.

Splashdown Waterbirth Services
✉ 17 Wellington Terrace, Harrow-On-The-Hill, Middx. HA1 3EP
☎ 0181 422 9308
Water Birth pools – inflatable and fibreglass, available for four week hire period. Local Bristol pool depot.

BABY AND NURSERY EQUIPMENT

Anything Left-Handed
✉ 15 Avenue Road, Belmont, Sutton, Surrey SM2 6JD
☎ 0171 437 3910
Specialises in items for the left-handed – scissors, writing equipment, kitchen and garden utensils. Send stamps for catalogue – call first to check current postage.

Bright Start
✉ 107 Regent's Park, London NW1 8UR
☎ 0171 483 3929
Brightly coloured gadgets for babies plus a good range of creative play toys and storage ideas from birth to toddler.

Firstborn
✉ 32 Bloomfield Avenue, Bath BA2 3AB
☎ 01225 422586
Wunderpants, Wundervests and Danish-style cloth nappies – natural fibre undergarments. Environmentally friendly alternative to disposables. Knit-your-own kits.
You can make an appointment to view products.

The Great Little Trading Company
✉ 134 Lots Road, London SW10 ORJ
☎ 0990 673 009
Sort of an Innovations catalogue for babies - storage, safety, lighting, toys, sun and rain gear and more- all well designed.

Huggababy
✉ 33 Deanswit Close, Goodrich, Herefordshire, HR9 6HQ
☎ 01600 890569
A plain and simple cotton sling - a natural alternative to the pushchair or pram for babies up to the 30lb toddler.

Little Jem
✉ PO Box 11935, London SW11 1ZR
☎ 0171 223 3350
Beautifully illustrated birth announcement cards, with specially commissioned designs you won't find in the shops. Can be personalised. Printed to order and mailed if you wish - not cheap but a boon for busy working parents.

Sling Easy
✉ Kids in Comfort, 172, Victoria Road, Wargrave, Reading RG10 8AJ
☎ 01734 404942
Machine washable baby carrier from the US. Very wide range of fabrics and colours, well padded and easily adjustable. Sizes: Birth to 35 lbs.

Suantrai Slings
✉ 16a Ballyman Road, Bray, Co. Wicklow, Ireland
☎ 0171 499 9505
Comfortable cotton slings in beautiful fabrics - can be made in your own material if supplied. Variants for petite and taller parents.

Mail Order

Tenderjoy
✉ The Silk Story, Freepost LON 7712, London SE16 4BR ☎ 0171 231 9788
100% silk jersey baby wear. Soft, washable, non-inflammable and proven to help in cases of rashes and skin irritation. Birth to 2 years. Also a range of tea tree baby products.

Tiny Trends
✉ 15 Redbreast Road, Bournemouth, Dorset BH9 3AL ☎ 01202 523060
Clothing for premature and low birthweight babies - a good range of baby basics in 100% cotton in sizes for 3-5lbs and 5-8lbs.

Tripp Trapp Chairs
✉ Lundia, 39 Goodramgate, York YO1 2LS ☎ 01904 637442
Ergonomic, Scandinavian wooden highchairs that are good for posture and last into young adulthood. Also easily adapted for children with special needs.

Wilkinet Baby Carrier
✉ PO Box 20, Cardigan SA43 1JB ☎ 01239 831246
Well-designed fabric baby carrier which can be used from newborn. Ties at back, front or on hip and holds baby in a natural sitting position against the parent's body. Weather cape and matching dungarees also available. Fabric samples supplied.

NATURAL BEDDING/GREEN PRODUCTS

Auro Paints
✉ Unit 1, Goldstones Farm, Ashdon, Saffron Walden CB10 2LZ ☎ 01799 584888
Huge range of organic products including wallpaints, gloss paint, woodstains, shellacs and varnishes, colour washes, adhesives and homecare products.

The Bed-Side-Bed Company
✉ 98 Woodlands Avenue, Wanstead, London E11 3QY ☎ 0181 989 8233
Beech-wood baby bed that can be adjusted in height to fit alongside the parents' bed and later transformed into a cot/first bed.

The Fairchild Company
✉ Parsonage Lane, Kingston St. Mary, Taunton TA2 8AW
☎ 01823 451881
Made to order mattresses, pillows, duvets, quilts and comforters stuffed with wool from the company's own organic smallholding. All sizes from moses basket to adult kingsize.

Farmer John Quilts
✉ Gaer Farm, Cwmyoy, Abergavenny, Gwent NP7 7NE
☎ 01873 890345
Quilts and duvets handmade on a hill farm in the Black Mountains using cotton casings and wool from local sheep.

Full Moon Futons
✉ 20 Bulmershe Road, Reading, Berks. RG1 5RJ
☎ 0118 926 5648
Natural cot and/or floor mattresses in unbleached, undyed 100% pure cotton – easily rolled for travelling. Also adult futons.

The Green Store
✉ ADMAIL 641, Bath BA1 1AD
☎ 01672 542266
Wonderful range of unbleached cotton blankets, bed linen and towels – cool linen for summer or brushed for winter. Plus eco duvets and pillows with filling made from recycled PET bottles – hypoallergenic. Wide range of cleaning products which are mild on the skin and the environment. Also shop at Green Street, Bath 01225 427155.

Luxus
✉ Unit 6, Church Farm, Hatley St. George, Sandy, Beds. SG19 3HR
☎ 01767 650858
100% natural fibre mattresses - a mix of coir, hair and wool filling, free from chemical treatments. Summer and winter sides to the mattress for optimum seasonal temperatures.

Wilkes and Weaver
✉ Offa House, Offa Street, Hereford HR1 2LH
☎ 01432 268018
Mattresses, duvets, pillows and bolsters. Sizes: small crib/moses basket to kingsize. Pure wool fillings, 100% cotton coverings.

Bath with your Kids 75

Mail Order

CHILDREN'S FASHION – SHOES

Birkenstock
✉ The Boot Tree Ltd., 1 Addison Bridge Place, London W14 8XP
☎ 0800 132 194
Trendy German classics - jewel-bright leather sandals, clogs and lace-ups. Continental sizes 24-34. Not cheap, but next-size-up footbeds are supplied for the lace-ups to stretch and extend their wear. Postal repair service.

Bobux
✉ RML, 48 Abbotswood Road, Streatham, London SW16 1AW
☎ 0181 677 9468
Bright and cheerful New Zealand soft first shoes in primary-coloured leather. Birth to shoe size 6. No fixings, ankle-grip elastic is used. Non-slip leather safety sole is safe for toe-gripping toddlers.

Daisy Roots
✉ Highgate House, Creaton, Northampton NN6 8NN
☎ 01604 505616
Reasonably priced handmade leather babies boots in bright colours with cut-out leather motifs. Safe non-skid soles. Sizes birth-24 months.

Charles MacWatt Originals
✉ 7 Christmas Steps, Bristol BS1 5BS
☎ 0117 921 4247
Handmade leather boots, sandals and shoes. Catalogue and foot template supplied on request. 8 kids' styles in 8 colourways. Sizes 4 (baby) to 5 (youth). Rugged designs with hard wearing crepe soles. Shoes can be resoled and stretched to the next size when outgrown – at no extra cost.

Soled Out
✉ Unit 8, Saltash Business Park, Moorlands Industrial Estate, Saltash, Cornwall PL12 6LX
☎ 01572 841080
Handmade, leather lined leather shoes, ankle boots and sandals - range of six children's' styles in lovely colours. Pamphlet and leather offcuts supplied. Sizes 5-13. Also stretching and resizing service for extra growth offered - you pay postage only for this.

CHILDREN'S FASHION – CLOTHES

Bishopston Trading Company
✉ 193 Gloucester Road, Bishopston Bristol BS7 8BG
☎ 0117 924 5598
Cotton, silk and canvas separates. Wonderful range of colours and styles for 2-8 and 9-14 years. Fair trade company – profits benefit Indian workers Co-op. Fabric swatches supplied.

Blooming Babies/Blooming Kids
✉ PO Box 12F, Chessington, Surrey KT9 2LS
☎ 0181 391 0338
Interesting, brightly coloured machine washable cotton separates. Sizes: birth-2 years, 2-8years and 8-12 years. Good value.

Cotton Moon
✉ PO Box 280, London SE3 8DZ
☎ 0181 3050012
Clean-cut American 100% cotton comfortable play-clothes, basics and smarter mix and match separates – appealing bright colours. Reasonably priced. 6 months-8 years.

Cotton On
✉ Monmouth Place, Bath BA1 2NP
☎ 01225 461155
Comfy casual clothing:sportswear, night and underwear with flat seams in 100% cotton. Recommended for sensitive skins, eczema or skin allergy sufferers. Sizes 0-12 years.

Daisychain
✉ Monasterevan, Co. Kildare, Ireland
☎ 0145 525757
Delightful handknit jumpers and cardigans in 100% cotton or wool and traditional cable designs. From birth to 5 years. Gift wrapping service for birth presents and birthdays.

Kid's Stuff
✉ 10 Hensmans Hill, Bristol BS8 4PE
☎ 0117 970 6095
Well-priced 100% cotton separates in cheerful colours and prints. Also Jersey nightwear for your child and teddy to match!

Little Badger
✉ 6 Macaulay Road, London SW4 0QX
☎ 0171 498 4707

Mail Order

Absolutely fabulous designer knitwear in 100% cotton or wool - strong primary colours and trendy motifs on sweaters, hats, booties and T-shirts. Sizes 0-10 years.

Little Elefant Kiri
✉ 493 Fulham Palace Road, London SW6 6SU
☎ 0171 610 6830
Traditional party dresses, coats, knitwear, nightwear. Seasonal catalogues. 0-10 years.

Mini Boden
✉ Midland Terrace, Victoria Road, London NW10 6DB
☎ 0181 453 1535
Good colour range – modern basics and more traditional styles. Wider range of pyjamas than the shops. Sizes 0-12 years.

Nipper
✉ Gloucester House, 45 Gloucester Street, Brighton BN1 4EW
☎ 01273 693785
Hard wearing practical clothes. Traditional materials and prints. Birth to 11 years. Fabric swatches sent on request.

Raindrops
✉ Pookles Lane, East Worldham, Alton, Hampshire GU34 3AT
☎ 01420 86933
Stylish Scandinavian outdoor clothing in red, green or navy blue, dungarees, jackets, hats and mittens that are waterproof and windproof as well as light and soft. Sizes 8 months-8 years.

Roobarb and Custard
☎ 0171 835 0010
Original, fashion-conscious clothes in bold styles - just like Mum and Dad would wear if they still went clubbing. 2-8 years.

Sweet Pea
✉ 119 Calvert Road, London SE10 ODG
☎ 0181 305 1229
Funky separates, for ages 6 months to 8 years, knitted or crocheted in strong colours. 100% cable cotton. Not cheap, but highly original.

Zed
✉ PO Box 9696, London NW6 1WE
Simple, streetwise designs in top fashion colours. Affordable and practical. For 2-8 years.

BOOKS AND CD ROMS

Barefoot Books
✉ Tiptree Book Services, Church Road, Tiptree, Essex CO5 OSR
☎ 0171 704 6492
High quality, beautifully illustrated books from cultures all over the world for ages 1-12. An inspiring selection.

Books For Children
✉ PO Box 413, Uxbridge, Middx UB11 1DX
For children aged 6 months to 12 years.
Sends 13 magazines a year plus seasonal specials. Opening offers (4 books for 50p each, plus gift). You must buy three more books in first year and decline recommended selection each month if it's not wanted.
Over 500 titles a year, with savings up to 50% off publishers' prices.
It's worth checking bookshop prices for paperback editions as 'publisher's price' sometimes refers to cost of hardback books.

CD Concepts
✉ Unit 2, Concord Business Centre, Acton, London W3 OTH
☎ 0181 993 7117
Good range of CD ROM titles from all the major publishers. Has some discounted titles.

Cyberomics
✉ Red Barn, Salisbury Road, Romsey SO51 6EE
☎ 01794 323606
Drily presented catalogue offering choice of educational and leisure CD ROM software plus hardware. Will price match.

Letterbox Library
✉ Unit 2D, Leroy House, 436 Essex Road, London N1 3QP ☎ 0171 226 1633
Selection of non-sexist, multi-cultural titles. Some overseas books not easily obtainable elsewhere plus useful issue-based selection. Quarterly catalogue - around 150 titles, tapes,

Mail Order

posters and CD ROMS. 10-25% discounts. Nursery to teenage. Must buy three books in first year. Local contact visits schools and groups ☎ 01225 334820.

Puffin Book Club

✉ c/o Penguin Books, 27 Wrights Lane, London W8 5TZ
☎ 0171 416 3135
Nursery or school class run, usually by teachers, leaders or parents with free Puffin book incentives for organising group. Six mailings per academic year. Discounts. Two magazines, posters, teachers' resources, and book week packs. 0-6 years, 6-9 years and 9-13 years.

The Red House

✉ Witney, Oxford OX8 5YF
☎ 01993 779090
Monthly catalogue of over 100 titles. Hard and paperback. No books sent unless ordered by you. Usual discount 25%. Joining offer. Must take three books in first year. Games, books, tapes, CD ROMS (separate catalogue), adult books also offered.

ROMRATS CD-ROM Club

✉ Freepost 1273, PO Box 300, Fareham, Hants PO14 1BR
£19.95 annual membership. 3 CD ROMs with sample demos of over 100 titles, selected for ease of use and educational content. 3-12 years.

TOYS AND GIFTS

Baby Basics

✉ PO Box 246, Southampton, Hants. SO14 OZL
☎ 01703 234949
Birth to 5 years. Informative catalogue with clear age suggestions. US-style products you won't find in the shops. No TV or violent toys.

Community Playthings

✉ Robertsbridge, East Sussex TN32 5DR
☎ 0800 387 457
Craftsman made solid maple play furniture, climbing frames and toys for nurseries and playgroups at affordable prices. Wonderful range of innovative ideas. Products devised by the Bruderhof Christian Community.

Countrywide Workshops Charitable Trust

✉ 47 Fisherton Street, Salisbury SP2 7SU
☎ 01722 411092
Beautifully made wooden toys, games, moses baskets and other household products, traditionally crafted by disabled people with all proceeds to charitable trust.

Early Learning Centre Mail Order

✉ South Marston Park, Swindon SN3 4TJ
☎ 0990 352352
Order from the catalogue of this popular, well-priced high street chain for home delivery at a reasonable price. Mostly for large play equipment.

The Faerie Shop By Post,

✉ PO Box 604, Marlborough, Wiltshire SN8 3NR
☎ 01672 871001
Ethereal faerie costumes, shoes and dressing-up accessories for ages 2-10.

Flip Flop Puzzle Mats

✉ 6 Harton Grove, South Shields, NE34 6LT
Non-slip, wipe-clean, cushioned brightly coloured jigsaw floor coverings. Excellent for soft play at nurseries, playgroups, schools.

The Green Board Game Company

✉ 34 Amersham Hill Drive, High Wycombe HP13 6QY
☎ 01494 538999
Highly educational but fun-looking board games on animal, global and environmental themes for ages 4-12.

The Hill Toy Company

✉ PO Box 100, Ripon, North Yorkshire HG4 4XZ
☎ 01765 689955
Very appealing traditional toys, for children up to about 10 years. Particularly good fancy dress and 'Picture products': your child's own "artwork" can be printed onto plate, clock, bowl or beaker.

Infant Isle Products

✉ Frank Whittle Business Centre, Great Central Way, Rugby CV21 3XH
☎ 01788 537893
Imaginative toys and baby gifts. A sort of Innovations for kids. Baby to primary age.

Mail Order

Jakada
✉ Freepost EH3604, Edinburgh EH5 OFE
☎ 0131 552 9988
Classic fancy dress for 3-8s, plus well-made toys not necessarily available in high street.

Letterbox
✉ Gerrans, Portscatho, Truro TR2 5ET
☎ 01872 580886
Lively selection of presents, toys and games, birth to teenage. Personalised gifts: mugs, pyjamas, hand painted chairs with recipient's name. Under £5 party and stocking fillers.

The Lifetime Company
✉ 5, Moorbridge Court, Moorbridge Road East, Nottingham NE13 8QG
☎ 01949 836360
Wide range of well designed educational toys made in traditional materials. Distribute soft play equipment.

Maple Valley Toy Company
✉ 3 Chilford Court, Braintree, Essex CM7 2QS
☎ 01376 321162
Reasonably priced range of well-made wooden toys. Rocking horse, doll's crib, hobby horse, xylophone, personalised wooden clock etc.

NES Arnold
✉ Ludlow Hill Road, West Bridgford NG2 6HD
☎ 0115 945 2201
Huge catalogue of pre-school toys, the "bible" for nursery school and playgroup leaders. Useful Early Years Curriculum Resources leaflet cross-references products according to educational criteria.

Orchard Toys
✉ Debdale Lane, Keyworth, Nottingham NG12 5HN ☎ 0115 937 3547
Well-illustrated jigsaw puzzles and games with a strong emphasis on learning through fun.

Rhyme & Reason Toys
✉ 2-5 Old Bond Street, London W1X 3TB
☎ 0171 499 9192
US import construction toys in painted maple and non-toxic foam for pre-schoolers.

Rifton
✉ Robertsbridge, East Sussex TN23 5DR
☎ 0800 387 531
Wonderfully comprehensive range of equipment designed for the child with special needs to play at school and at home.

Tous Mes Amis
✉ PO Pox 154, Farnham, Surrey GU9 8YD
☎ 01252 733188
French children's favourites: Babar, the Little Prince, Asterix, Madeline and Becassine in all their many incarnations. Videos, books, toys, tableware, stationery and more.

Treasure Chest
✉ The Old School, 1 High Street, Tattenhall CH3 9PX
☎ 01829 770787
Bright hand-made wooden toys for example: castle, farmhouse, puppet theatre etc, plus hand sewn wallhangings and colourful pre-school learning games.

Tribale
✉ PO Box 15, Earl Shilton, Leicester LE9 8WA
☎ 01455 852533
Multicultural play ideas: a beautiful play tipi, global string games and make your own moccasin kit. Proceeds to Survival, worldwide organisation in support of tribal peoples.

Tridias Toys By Post
✉ 124 Walcot Street, Bath BA1 5BG
☎ 0990 133 002
Traditional toys, games and activity gifts from birth to teenage. Sections for dressing up and party props.

OUTDOOR PLAY EQUIPMENT

Air Mail
✉ PO Box 1580, Bath BA1 3TJ
☎ 01225 466999
Kites, boomerangs, frisbees, yoyos, rockets and all manner of unidentified flying objects.

Eibe Play
✉ Forest House, 8 Baxter Road, Sale M33 3AL
At prices beyond the pockets of most families,

Mail Order

but a very well-designed range of teepees, wooden log-cabins, rockers and chalets for outdoor and indoor play. 350 page catalogue available - send £3.50 cheque.

Kiddie Wise

✉ PO Box 433, Leek, Staffs. ST13 7TZ
☎ 01538 304235
Outdoor play equipment from sustainable timber sources. Built to last, priced accordingly.

Super Tramp

✉ Langlands, Uffculme, Cullompton,
Devon EX15 3DA
☎ 01884 841305
Not the late 70's pop combo, but purveyors of serious outdoor trampolines for family fitness use and fun.

Tall Ships Playframes

✉ Highfield Road Industrial Estate,
Camelford PL32 9RA
☎ 01840 212022
Imaginative pirate-style wooden playframes, canvas accessories with swingboats, jungle bridges, deathslide(!) and even a crows nest. Scallywag children's wooden rowing boats and sailing craft for 2-7 years.

PARTY ITEMS AND STOCKING FILLERS

Hawkin By Post

✉ St Margaret, Harleston, Norfolk IP20 OPJ
☎ 01986 782536
Eccentric collection of puzzles, oddities and curiosities, clearly marked if not suitable for children (eg. tin collectors' toys). Something for everyone, often at pocket money prices.

Party Pieces

✉ Child's Court Farm, Ashampstead Common, Berkshire RG8 8QT ☎ 01635 201844
Everything for children's parties from invites to dressing up and going home presents.

Stocking Fillas

✉ Euroway Business Park, Swindon SN38 2NN
☎ 0990 250990
Christmas catalogue, hundreds of novelties and party toys, many under £1. Clearly marked if small enough for homemade Christmas crackers. Also Party-Party catalogue - party kits from £20.

U-Need-Us

✉ 30 Arundel Street, Portsmouth PO1 1NW
☎ 01705 823013
Full selection of carnival, dance and party goods, balloons, decorations, flags and pennants, grease paint and masks. Plus tombola, bingo books and tickets for fund raising.

Parks and Play Areas

Bath has an excellent choice of parks and play areas, many have been refurbished over the last few years. Play areas are fenced, with soft surfaces, good equipment, some shade and adult seating, unless otherwise stated. Many play areas are local facilities, but good to visit if you are in the area, those worth a special visit are indicated. Equipment is checked weekly and daily in some of the heavily used areas.

Dogs are banned in all play areas and pooper scooper areas operate most parks. Dogs must be on leads in the Botanical Gardens in Victoria Park and Henrietta Park scented garden. A dog warden operates in Bath.

Uncovered sandpits can be a source of TOXOPLASMOSIS, usually a mild glandular type fever in children, rarely with complications. Infection in pregnancy can be more serious, so care should be taken, even though dogs are banned from such areas.

Easy parking, single and double buggy access is available unless indicated.

Council Parks Department
☎ 396021
Contact the Parks Department if you are aware of any problems or have comments to make concerning Bath's parks or play areas.

Badgerline Bus
☎ 464446
Routes from the city centre bus station are shown. A bus route map of Bath and the surrounding area is available from the Bus station information office.

National Playing Fields Association
✉ 25 Ovington Square, London SW3 1LQ
☎ 0171 584 6445.
Concerned about the loss of playing fields to building development. Also provide advice on design of equipment for play areas.

PARK EVENTS

For information contact Sarah Giovanni at the Council Parks Department ☎ 396021.

Balloon Ascents
Mainly during the summer at Royal Victoria Park, Pennyquick and Newbridge Open Spaces. Balloons take off mornings and evenings on still days.

Band Concerts
Parade Gardens (free for residents with proof), May to September every Sunday and Bank Holiday. Royal Victoria Park, Sydney Gardens and Alice Park, May to September every Sunday.

Bath Children's Festival
Part of the Bath Festival during summer half term weekend. See **Annual Events**.

Bath Festival Opening Night
On the grassy area below Royal Crescent. Dusk opening ceremony includes band, fireworks and candles.

Children's Summer Entertainment
Magic, puppets, theatre and more in Parade Gardens, late July and August (not Bank Holidays.) Weekday afternoons 3pm. Free entry to residents with proof.

Playschemes
Use parks during summer, sometimes with entertainment. See council playschemes literature (see **Activities and Clubs**).

Spring Flower Show
Every May Day Bank Holiday weekend in Royal Victoria Park. Free for accompanied children under 16. Free WRVS crèche with provision for breastfeeding mothers.

Parks and Play Areas

Parks and Play Areas in Detail

See Map on Pages 138/9

1. Alexandra Park
⌦ Bear Flat Buses 3 and 14. Car access from top of Shakespeare Avenue or walk uphill from Greenway Lane (Kissing Gate) or Holloway (awkward entrance). For an interesting arrival puff up Jacob's Ladder, a long flight of steps from Alexandra Road. Great views, especially on Firework nights. Sledge carefully, watching out for circling cars and enjoy cool breezes on hot days. Lovely spacious feel, big trees and pine cones. Suitable for all ages but play area less appealing for juniors. Toddler swings and others, seesaw, climbing frame with slide, helter skelter and ride ons. Loos but no shelter.

2. Alice Park
⌦ At junction of A4 and the now quiet Gloucester Road. Buses 13,13a and 13b. Limited parking in park. Watch tennis at the top end, or pond life in unfenced pond. Large play area, huge, popular sandpit with crane and mini diggers, helter skelter, spider climbing frame, toddler tyre, other swings and ride-ons. Picnic tables. Loos and a lovely café open weekends during the summer.

3. Ballance Street
⌦ Lower Lansdown. Bus No. 2 to Julian Road. Behind houses and flats in Ballance Street and Morford Street. Two hour parking. A high slide and huge climbing frame surrounded by trees and flats. Toddler slide, two toddler swings, other swings and ride-on.

4. Bathford Play Area
⌦ Ashley Road, Bathford. Buses 13 and 13a. Go up main hill and turn left, before Hairdressers. Play area is on the left, through large iron gates, opposite No.6. A little gem with roundabout, stage coach climber and slide, seesaw, two toddler swings and others, two riders and a three seater rocker horse, noughts and crosses and other activities.

5. Beacon Hill
⌦ Lansdown. Bus No. 2 to St Stephens Church. Up Lansdown Road, Richmond Road and Richmond Place to St Stephen's School. Play area is opposite, bounded by residential roads and a grassy area but no fences. Difficult to park. Views across Beechen Cliff. Toddler and tyre swings, climbing frame and roundabout. Watch out for dogs. Ball games inadvisable. Avoid end-of-School times if you have toddlers.

6. Beazer Maze
⌦ Pulteney Weir, below Pulteney Bridge before Bath Rugby Club. On foot, down steps from Argyle Street or push buggy down Grove Street and through tunnel. Not signposted. Excellent break from the agonies of shopping for parents (who can put feet up on low wall) and children, who can let off steam. Simple open air maze of paving slabs on grass reaching an attractive mosaic in the centre. Challenging for 4-7 year olds. Sun trap with mature trees providing shade for picnic.

7. Bloomfield Road
⌦ Bloomfield. Buses 3, 13a, 14, 14a and 14b. From Bear Flat turn right into BLoomfield Road. Park is on the right after 100 yards. Play area at top end of large sloping field. Two swings, one toddler swing, balance discs with poles. Large sandpit with cranes, poles and wide slide.

8. Brassmill Lane Open Space
⌦ Newbridge. Buses 336, 337, 339 and x39. Follow signs to Brassmill Lane Trading Estate. At Locksbrook Road end. Lovely climbing frame, toddler and other slide, swings and roundabout. Open space bounded by one busy road.

9. Brickfield
⌦ Oldfield Park, Twerton, Lymore Avenue. Buses 12 and 12a. Park opposite Rising Sun and take track between no. 84 and Nursing Home. Large field with good size play area. Tyre swing, two toddler swings and two others. Large slide, climber and aerial disc swing. Best for juniors.

10. Calton Road
⌦ Lyncombe Hill. Buses 2 and 4. Second right off hill into Calton Road, park is above road after 100yards. Train spotters delight! Birds eye view of Bath Spa Station and city centre. Steep path to Alexandra Park starts here. Shady and a bit lonely. Smallish area with walkway and large slide, swing, two ride-ons and interesting rockface to climb. Preschool or primary ages.

82 Bath with your Kids

Parks and Play Areas

11. Chandler Close
◽ Weston. Bus No 17. Next to Weston Primary school and back of hospital. From Kelston Road, turn into Penn Hill Road and fifth left into Chandlers Close. Preschool play area, with two swings, slide and odd tyre tree next to No.52. Toddlers area, with two toddler swings, slide, three ride-ons and climbing ladder next to No 18. Small areas with limited parking.

12. Corston View
◽ Upper Bloomfield. Bus No. 14b. Up Bloomfield Drive, right into Somerdale Avenue and right into Corston View. Park near No.30, walk towards TV mast and park is on the right. Access on foot also from Bloomfield Drive. Double buggy access difficult. Wonderful views across to Weston and city from this exposed site with adjoining fields. Chain and plank climbing frame with slide, igloo climb-frame, alligator ride-on, toddler slide, tyre and toddler swings. Look out for broken glass.

13. Cranmore Place
◽ Odd Down. Bus 14a. Over roundabout at top of Wellsway, second left into Banwell Road, left again and right into Cranmore Place. Park near school entrance, gate to park is opposite and difficult to spot squeezed in behind the back of houses. An unexpected delight with adventure play circuit with walkway, wide slide, aerial rope slide, rotating tyre swing and three other tyre swings. Lovely playhouse, slide, roundabout and ride-on for toddlers. No shade.

14. Dartmouth Avenue
◽ Oldfield Park/Twerton. Buses 12 and 12a. Access from Lymore Gardens, a dead end off Lymore Avenue. Preschool age, small area with large climbing frame with slide, three toddler swings, two ride-ons and rope ladder. No shade.

15. Dorset Close
◽ Lower Bristol Road, Twerton. Bus No.5 From the Lower Bristol Road, past Windsor Bridge turn left into Dorset Close and park near School. Access also from Denmark Street and Dorset Street. Tiny urban play area for pre-schoolers and younger. Two toddler and two tyre swings, a slide, seesaw, two small ladders, a ride-on and a small roundabout.

16. Dunstar House
◽ Meare Road, Foxhill. Buses 3 and 13a. For local residents. Small grassy toddler area with slide, ride-on and play house.

17. Firsfield
◽ Combe Down. Buses 2,4 and 13a. Top of Ralph Allen Drive into The Avenue or The Firs to park. Double buggy access difficult. Breezy play area with picnic benches but no shade. 4 toddler swings and 8 others. Seesaw, helter skelter slide, ride-ons, bus climbing frame with slide. Large open space great for ball games.

18. Excelsior Street
◽ Widcombe. Buses 2 or 4. From Pulteney Road turn left into Broadway and left into Archway. Head for railway arches. Teeney toddler play area with climbing frame, swing and wide slide.

19. Green Park
◽ City Centre, off Green Park Road. Near pedestrian entrance to Sainsburys. Limited on-street, paying parking. Conker trees and dog-poo on this unfenced, flat grassy space, unrestricted access for dogs. Swings – toddler and other, roundabout and elephant ride-on. Relatively unattractive, but closest running-around space to Sainsburys. On riverside walk.

20. Hedgemead Park
◽ Walcot/Camden. Buses 2, 8 and 9. Level pedestrian access off Lansdown Road or uphill from London Road and Guinea Street or downhill from Caroline Place. Difficult parking. Pleasant sloping park with preschool play area. Four toddler swings and four tyre swings, seesaw, roundabout and lovely climbing frame with slide.

21. Henrietta Park
◽ Bathwick. Bus No.4 to Great Pulteney Street. Access from Henrietta Street, Road, Mews or Gardens. Two hour parking area. No fence between park and road. Large mature trees regally spaced across pleasant lawns with flowerbeds. Good for picnics and shuffling through autumn leaves. Fenced off scented gardens with fountain and pond (not fenced). Loos.

Parks and Play Areas

22. Homemead Park
✉ Weston. Bus No 7. Upper end of Purlewent Drive next to electricity substation. Look out for Cotswold Way sign, go up track opposite to garages. Entrance sometimes locked on this sloping side. Mixed age appeal with toddler area with climbing frame, two slides and noughts and crosses. Second area has large climbing frame with big slide, ropes and poles and rock climbing face.

23. Innox Park
✉ Twerton. Buses 12 and 12a. From Twerton High Street turn left into Watery Lane, next left into Freeview Road, park is at the end. Access on foot, over the playing field from The Brow and Kelston View. Double buggies are a squeeze through Freeview Road kissing gate. Large sloping field with views to Weston. Play area has a tyre swing which hangs off a crane, disc swing plus wooden ramp to launch off. Slide and climbing frame, toddler swing and ride-ons. Beware occasional broken glass.

24. Kelston Field
✉ Weston, Windsor Bridge. Buses 14, 14a, 14b, 17, 331, 332, 336, 337, 339 and X39. After Windsor Bridge turn left down a side road before Locksbrook Road, next to newsagent. Limited parking in unmade road. Small shade corner behind houses and river walk. A tiny play area for toddlers with swing, slide, tyre swing, log climbing frame and two small ladders.

25. Kingsway
✉ Southdown/Bloomfield. Buses 16 and 17. Find Post Office at upper end of Englishcombe Lane, opposite Sladesbrook Road. Turn left into Kingway. Take track on left hand side after 200yards to garages. Park is on the left. Tucked away from traffic, with toddler swing, tyre swings and others, ride-ons, large climbing frame with slides, poles and walkways.

26. Larkhall Recreation
✉ Larkhall. Bus No.8. Entrances opposite St Mark's and St Saviour's schools in Charlecombe Lane and Brooklyn Road. Rough buggy walk across field to play area. Good for ball games away from traffic. Toddler swings, tyre swings, carriage with slide, two ride-ons and a climbing frame.

27. Loxton Drive
✉ Twerton. Bus No.5. From Lower Bristol Road turn left into Lansdown View Road, right into Albany Road and left into Luxton Close, park. Tiny play area for preschool and toddlers. Pair of seal ride-ons, climbing frame with small and large slide.

28. Midsummer Buildings
✉ Fairfield. Bus No.9 From Fairfield Road take third right into Midsummer Buildings. Park is on the right down near No.45. Pleasant grassed play area suitable for preschool and juniors. Two tyre swings, pair of seesaws, two ride-ons and balancing activities. Lovely little sandpit with mini digger and popular play house.

29. Moorlands Recreation Ground
✉ Englishcombe. Buses 10 and 11.
Off Englishcombe Lane behind Moorlands Junior School. Entrance halfway between Bloomfield Park and Oak Avenue. Sloping field with lovely trees suitable for ball games, sledging and autumn walk. Play area built of rough-hewn wood. Tyre and other swings, slide and climbing frame. Most suitable for juniors.

30. Moorlands Sandpits
✉ Monksdale Road. Bus No.7. Entrance at junction with Hillside Road. Sail small boats down the shallow channelled stream which winds though the middle of this grassy play area/park. Lots of imaginatively designed climbing equipment. Water wheel tower, helicopter climbing frame and walkway. Toddler and other swings, ride-ons, seesaw, slide, helter skelter and sandpit. Take buckets and spades. Loos. Great location for preschool group picnics. Watching more than one toddler can be stressful because there's a stream and hilly area at top end can hide children from view, but well worth a visit.

31. Mount Road
✉ Twerton/Southdown. Buses 10 and 11. Near top of Englishcombe Lane, turn right into Mount Road, past schools. Pudding shaped hill is on the left. Wonderful panoramic views at the top of Bath and Englishcombe valley. Great for Kite flying. Lots of wildlife. Play area has slide, toddler swings and others, ride-ons and circular swinger. Loos.

Parks and Play Areas

32. Newbridge Open Space

Buses 336,337,339 and X39. At corner of Newbridge Road and Brassmill Lane, next to caravan park. Flat field with lovely avenue of trees for chasing and hiding, but no hard ball games allowed. A large tyre swing and small bouncy tractors.
Also sandpit, slide, toddler swings, climbing frame, playhouse and picnic benches. For preschool and younger.

33. Parade Gardens

City Centre by Abbey, below Orange Grove and North Parade. Entrance by Empire hotel. Open Easter to end of September. Free entry for residents of Bath and North East Somerset with proof, charge for others over five.
An oasis of peace away from city centre bustle. Lovely formal gardens with much admired feature flower bed (cartoon characters etc) which changes annually.
By the river and weir (which is fenced) so great for duck feeding and watching boats and canoes (you can also see quite big fish too!). Racing up and down the colonnades good in a rain shower (watch out for pigeon poo). Deck chairs for hire, watch summer Sunday concerts in the bandstand and free children's entertainment on summer holiday afternoons (see **Annual Events**). Loos and baby changing (ask at kiosk for key – see **Loo Stops**). Picnics allowed also café, with outdoor seating, for drinks, ice-creams and snacks.

34. Parry Close

Southdown. Buses 10 and 11. From bottom of Southdown Road turn left into Parry Close, follow road around several sharp turns and park is near No.47. Limited parking. Tiny shaded play area with three ride-ons, two toddler swings and toddler slide.

35. Pennyquick Open Space

Old Twerton. Bus No.5. Off Newton Road on right after Day Crescent. Cross football pitches to reach two adjoining play areas. Lovely windy open space close to fenced wood.
Toddler area has slide, three swings, two ride-ons and seesaw. Preschool/junior section has slide, seesaw, caterpillar and tank climbing frames, spider frame and four swings.

36. Rosewarn Close

Whiteway. Buses 5,12 and 12a. Up The Hollow near top turn right from mini roundabout into Haycombe Drive, left at the T junction and right into Rosewarn Close.
Park near No 37 for shady preschool area with helter skelter and other slide, climbing frame and two swings. No benches. Park near No. 71 for the Adventure play area. A huge area inside a stockade for junior or older. Two crane/tyre swings, aerial ropeway, ram swing, assault rope, hanging bars, two seesaw swings and slide built into hill. Skateboard area.
A little graffiti, but best facilities outside Victoria Park for older children. Two play areas are too far apart to supervise simultaneously.

37. Roundhill Park

Twerton. Buses 10, 11 and 12. From Haycombe Cemetery turn right into The Hollow and first right into Roundhill Park. Small play area in centre of oval road. Sunny green surrounded by road with small shady play area in the middle with tyre and toddler swing, climbing frame, slide and toddler seesaw. Suit toddlers and pre-schoolers.

38. Royal Victoria Park

Lower Weston, Upper Bristol Road. Buses 17, 14, 14a, 14b, 331 and 332. Leaving Bath on the A4 (going towards Bristol), park is on the right after Marlborough Lane. Parking on circular road inside park (busy at weekends/holidays), access from Park Lane or Royal Avenue. Must be the best park and public adventure play area for miles. Park includes botanical gardens at Weston Road end with steep woodland grove, squirrels and doves. Pond for model boats and duck feeding. Beneath Royal Crescent are tennis courts, small café, bowling green, small aviary and pitch and putt. Hot air balloons regularly take off after 6pm or holidays. Fairs are held in the NE corner. The adventure play area is huge and imaginative with lots for all ages. Equipment is grouped roughly according to age which is difficult if you have more than one age group to watch. Exceptionally busy on Sundays and holidays and can be a bit overwhelming for tinies. Kids love it and over threes are generally okay. Younger children need lots of help. Lots of swings, climbers and slides of all sorts. Toddlers train and station, sand cranes, sit on

Bath with your Kids 85

Parks and Play Areas

horses and carriage. A small hill includes jungle trail, walkways, aerial runway, tunnel slides, boats and large tyre swing. Skateboard area near play area. All day park Supervisor on duty with lost children area. Adult loos just outside and children only loos inside area. Shade, shelter and seating - great for picnics. The ever present ice cream van is just outside the gate and there is a 'pay' bouncy castle and roundabout at peak times.

39. Snow Hill
▣ Walcot. Buses 13 and 13a. Go up Snow Hill and park near second left turning. Toddler/preschool area is tucked behind buildings on the left. All weather surface overlooked by flats: twin tower climbing frame with slide and ladders, ride-ons, roundabout and small sandpit with mini diggers. Second area is up a bit on the right for preschool and juniors. Extends over three tiers with ride-ons, roundabout, swing and interesting slide set into hill with rope ladders. Large climbing frame with slides and poles.

40. Springfield Farm
▣ Foxhill. Buses 3 and 13a. From Foxhill turn into Queen Drive and left into Meare Road. Park near No.23. High windy open space with views over Bath. Plenty of room to kick a ball. Goal posts and skateboard area. Two linked fenced areas. Toddler area has two toddler swings, a pair of ride-on black horses and slide. Second area has log bars, ball and socket tyre swing and unusual seesaw.

41. St Saviour's Open Space
▣ Larkhall. Bus No.8. From Larkhall village follow St Saviour's Road. Park near Brooklyn Road turning on left. Park is on the right over stream. Small play area for toddlers and preschool with three toddler swings, slide, climbing frame and two ride-ons. No shade.

42. Sydney Gardens
▣ Bathwick. Buses 4 and 18. Immediately behind Holbourne Museum at end of Great Pulteney Street (tea room). Parking can be difficult on Warminster Road. Single buggy access only from canal path, but easy access from other entrances. Formal city gardens with flower beds, gracious trees, squirrels, wide paths for ride-ons and bikes. Most loved for bridge views of railway line for train spotting and access to canal for duck feeding. Tennis courts, bowling green and architectural shelters. Loos.
Play area is at top left end of park with two levels. Toddler and other swings, seesaw, roundabout and large slide with wide wooden log steps in sandpit.

43. Valley View Close
▣ Larkhall. Bus No.8. Steep walk up Valley View Road, take fourth left into Close. Small park of astro-turf with long slide set into a hill with climbing ropes, climbing frame and swing. Small sandpit and four seater bouncer. No shade. Toddlers and pre-schoolers.

44. Weston Recreation Ground
Bus No. 17. Turn into Southlands from Penn Hill Road. Park near No. 72. Large grassy area with views across city and to racecourse. Walks onto hills start here. Play area has slide dug into hill side, wooden climbing frame, tyre, toddler and other swings and bouncy seesaw. Outside play area is lovely large tree with picnic tables.

45. Widcombe Open Space
Buses 2 and 4. From Pulteney Road turn into Broadway, left into Archway Street and left into Princes Buildings. Park is on the right near school. Popular with mums picking up from school. Large play area with lots of grass behind a good fence, but along side a busy main road. Two toddler and four other swings, climbing frame, toddler slide and large slide.

46. Woodhouse Park
▣ Twerton. Bus No.5. From Twerton High Street take 2nd right into Woodhouse Road. Follow signs to No's 1-7, park near garages. Play area tucked away behind flats near junior school. Sunny spot for babies and toddlers. Two toddler swings, slide, four way bouncer, seesaw, two swings, two ride-ons and a spider ladder.

Places of Worship

Here is a selection of the many places of worship in and around Bath that offer specific family or children's services and crèches. Several Churches run Holiday Clubs (see Activities and Clubs). The list is not exhaustive. For those faiths which do not have local facilities we have included those in Bristol. We have tried to locate as many denominations as we could contact; if any are ommited, it is not intentional.

CENTRAL BATH

Bath Abbey
✉ Kingston Buildings ☎ 422462
9.15am Parish Communion and Children's Group
Crèche available.

Bath City Church
✉ 1 Forum Buildings, St. James ☎ 463556
10am Service, Sunday School and Crèche.

Central United Reformed Church
☎ 310050
10.30am Service with crèche and Junior Church.

Christ Church
✉ Julian Road ☎ 338869
10am Family Communion, Junior Church, 3 age groups and crèche.

Friends Meeting House
✉ York Street ☎ 469555
Meeting for Worship, 10.45-11.45am includes children's session.

Hay Hill Baptist
✉ The Paragon ☎ 422604
11am Service, crèche and Sunday School.

Holy Trinity C of E
✉ Queens Square ☎ 423718
10am Service with Sunday School

Manvers Street Baptist
☎ 461600
10.30am Service, Sunday School and crèche.

St. John the Evangelist, Roman Catholic
✉ South Parade ☎ 464471
Family Mass at 9.30am.

St. Mary the Virgin C of E
✉ Bathwick ☎ 460052
10.30am Service, Sunday School for under 10s, crèche provided.

St. Matthews
✉ Widcombe Hill ☎ 310580
Morning Service 10.30am, 2nd and 4th Sunday – Family Service, other weeks Sunday school.

St. Michael with St. Paul C of E
✉ Broad Street ☎ 835490
11am Service, crèche and Sunday School. Family Service first Sunday of each month.

St. Thomas a Becket
✉ Church Lane, Widcombe ☎ 310580
10.30am, 1st and 3rd Sunday, Sunday School, all other weeks. Children very welcome.

Salvation Army
✉ Green Park Road ☎ 310425
10am Service, children very welcome. Sunday School 11.15am-12.15pm

Walcot Methodist Church
✉ London Road ☎ 464371
10.30am Morning Service with Junior Church for children aged 3 years and over. Crèche.

Widcombe Baptist
✉ Pulteney Road, Widcombe ☎ 316358
10.30am Service with crèche and Sunday School for three age ranges. Seekers, Searchers and Contact groups held on Fridays 6.30-7.45pm.

Bath with your Kids

Places of Worship

Larkhall, Fairfield Park and Lansdown

Claremont Methodist Church
✉ Claremont Road ☎ 421343
Family Service once a month.

Larkhall United Reformed Church
✉ Dafford Street, Larkhall ☎ 832268
11am Service, Sunday School for age 3+.

St.Saviours C of E
✉ St.Saviours Road, Larkhall ☎ 311637
Junior Church/Crèche 10.45am Family Service first Sunday of each month.

St.Stephen's C of E
✉ Lansdown ☎ 317535
11am Service, Sunday Club for age 3+.

Batheaston, Bathford and Bathampton

Batheaston Congregational
✉ High Street, Batheaston
11am Service - children welcome.

Batheaston Methodist
✉ Northend, Batheaston ☎ 421343
10.30am Service - crèche available.

Bathampton Methodist
✉ Holcombe Lane, Bathampton ☎ 421343
11am Service - children welcome.

Good Shepherd RC
✉ Brow Hill, Batheaston ☎ 858845
11am - Children's liturgy as part of service.

St.John the Baptist
✉ Northend, Batheaston ☎ 858192
9.30am Service - Children's Church every week except 1st week of month when Family Service.

St.Nicholas C of E
✉ Bathampton ☎ 463570
10.30am Family Service once a month. Groups for children each Sunday

St.Swithun's C of E.
✉ Bathford ☎ 858325
10am Family Communion - 5-9 years Club during Service.

Weston and Newbridge

All Saints C of E
✉ Weston ☎ 421159
10.30am Family Service 1st Sunday of month. Children's Church and Crèche each week.

Emmanuel C. of E
✉ Apsley Road ☎ 427206
10am Service with Sunday School. Family Service 1st and 3rd Sunday of each month.

St.John the Evangelist C of E
✉ Upper Bristol Road, Lower Weston
☎ 427206
10am Family Service. Sunday School and crèche. Pram Service first Wednesday of month 10am Kings Club, 5-10 years, 5.45-7pm Friday. Open to everyone.

Weston Methodist
✉ High Street, Weston ☎ 421343
11am Service, children welcome.

Odd Down

Fosseway Community Church
✉ Fosseway Junior School, Odd Down ☎ 835228
Family Service 10.30am.

United Reformed Church
✉ Rush Hill ☎ 832268
10.30am Service, crèche if needed. Sunday School. Family Service every third Sunday of the month.

St.Phillip and St.James C of E
✉ Odd Down ☎ 835228
10.30am Family Service, 3rd Sunday of each month. Other Sundays, crèche and various Sunday Schools. Children's groups for 7-11 year olds Monday evenings 6-7.30pm.

Combe Down and Foxhill

Holy Trinity
✉ Combe Down ☎ 833152
All Age Family Worship at 9.30am with Sunday School and crèche. 3rd Sunday of the month children remain in main service.

Places of Worship

St. Andrew's C of E
✉ Foxhill ☎ 833152
11.15am Service with crèche.

St. Peter and St. Paul RC
Bradford Road, Combe Down ☎ 832096
Family Mass Sunday 9.30am with children's liturgy.

OLDFIELD PARK AND BEAR FLAT

Beechen Cliff Methodist
✉ Shakespeare Avenue ☎ 840918
10.30am Service and Junior Church 3-16 years.

Oldfield Park Methodist
✉ The Triangle ☎ 425230
11am Service, Sunday School for 3+ years, regular family services.

St. Alphege RC
✉ Oldfield Lane ☎ 424894
10.30am Mass, children welcome at all Services. 1st Sunday of the month Youth Sunday. Tuesday once a month pre-school mass 10.15-10.35am

St. Luke's C of E
✉ Wellsway ☎ 311904
10.30am Service, crèche and Sunday School. Family Service every third Sunday. Bible Study group with crèche alternate Thursdays 10.15am

TWERTON, SOUTHDOWN, SLADEBROOK AND ENGLISHCOMBE

Church of God of Prophesy
✉ Twerton Zion Methodist Church
☎ 425230
12noon Service with Sunday School and crèche.

The Salvation Army
✉ Haycombe Drive Whiteway
☎ 422673
Monday night 5.15-6.45pm Junior Club, age 4-10 years, games and drawing, very gentle Biblical theme - all welcome.

Southdown Methodist
✉ The Hollow ☎ 840918
11am Service children welcome with Junior Church 3-16 years.

Twerton Zion Methodist
☎ 425230
10.30 a.m. Service with Sunday School and crèche if needed. Family Service on regular basis.

Victory Christian Centre
✉ Englishcombe Lane
Children's Church 10am, Family Worship at 11am.

OTHERS

Bath Buddhists
☎ 722172

Bath Islamic Centre Al Muzafar Mosque
✉ Manvers Street ☎ 460922

Bahai Faith
✉ 40 Sheridan Road ☎ 426725
Children's programme being introduced. Open to anyone interested.

Greek Orthodox Church
✉ Berkeley Road, Westbury, Bristol
☎ 0117-973-335/935105
Children welcome to Services and playgroup held on Saturday mornings behind Church.

St. John of Krondstadt Orthodox
☎ 318338
Call for further information.

Sikh Resource Centre
✉ 114 St. Marks Road, Easton, Bristol
☎ 0117-952-5023/939-1120
Three different Punjabi language classes held for 5-14 years old.

Synagogue, Bristol and West Progressive Jewish Congregation
✉ Bannerman Road, Bristol ☎ 0117-954-1937
Religious school for 4-16 years Sunday morning.

Bath with your Kids 89

A major new title from Venue Publishing

The GOOD HEALTH Guide

- ◆ Editorial features
- ◆ A - Z of Treatments
- ◆ Health Facts & Figures
- ◆ Optimum Fitness Advice

A complete guide to looking after yourself and your family

"there is not one person in this area who would not benefit from the information contained in The Good Health Guide..."

The Guide costs £5, to order your copy call (0117) 942 8491 or write to Venue Publishing, 65 North Road, Bristol BS6 5AQ

Information for Informed choices

Pubs

The pubs listed in this section provide facilities for children. There are many pubs not listed here that may accept children but provide no facilities. It is worth checking these out yourself. For the pubs listed it is generally accepted that children are welcome but not past 9pm. Some pubs only offer inside facilities, others only outside ones, so bear the weather in mind when you choose them. Please also bear in mind that landlords take no responsibility for accidents that occur on their premises. You are responsible at all times.

MEALS: Some pubs offer a children's menu; others offer small portions. Most are prepared to supply an extra plate to split a standard menu if asked. Check on last-order times for meals. It is advisable to pre-book any available highchairs by phone.

TOILETS: Very few pubs provide nappy-changing facilities, but all the pubs listed below have clean presentable loos. It is advisable to take along a changing mat as you will usually have to change nappies on the floor of the Ladies. No Mens toilet was recommended!

THE LAW: Children are allowed into pubs accompanied by an adult, at the landlord's discretion and provided they sit in a room with no bar, or else outside.

LICENSING HOURS: The law says that pubs can stay open between 11am-11pm Monday to Saturday and 12pm-10.30pm Sunday. Since opening times vary, both seasonally and from pub to pub, it is best to check.

PUBS IN BATH

Bear Inn
◻ Bear Flat, Wellsway ☎ 425795
Open all day. Lunch 12-2pm. A lounge where children can eat. Restaurant menu featuring steaks, mixed grill, etc. The 'Bear Cub' children's menu, two highchairs. Easy access.

Blathwayt Arms
◻ Lansdown Road ☎ 421995
Open all day. Large family pub close to Bath Racecourse. Separate family dining area in bright conservatory catering for children of all ages. Highchairs, baby changing, children's menu and portions. Large garden with bouncy castle, slide, climbing frame. Parking no problem.

The Boater
◻ Argyle Street ☎ 464211
A busy city centre pub, that has a large courtyard beer garden down by the river which families can use. Serves food.

Crystal Palace
◻ Abbey Green ☎ 423994
Suitable eating areas for families inside and out at this city centre pub. It can get very crowded, and buggies would be a problem inside. Safe enclosed courtyard at the back, but with no children's equipment. Also an area at the back which is suitable if the weather's bad. Basic children's menu with occasional specials.

The Crown
◻ Bathwick Street (opposite Sydney Gardens) ☎ 429172
Imaginative menu with children's portions. No highchair, but colouring and toys on request. Outside, play equipment. Plenty of space, busy and comfortable. "Hard to beat this family pub".

Green Park Tavern
◻ Lower Bristol Road ☎ 400050
Basic pub fare with some vegetarian selections and small portions available. Well behaved children welcome in bar and dining area. Potentially smoky.

Pubs

Hare and Hounds
✉ Lansdown Road ☎ 425579
Open all day Monday–Saturday. Good selection of food and specials with a range of reasonably priced children's meals. Sizeable family room, also large garden and patio for fine weather with a few old climbing frames. Good views.

The Old Crown Inn
✉ 1 Crown Hill, Weston ☎ 423371
Children welcome at lunchtimes and early evening and are catered for on the menu. A walled garden with picnic tables, play equipment and bouncy castle. Spacious toilets.

Red Lion Harvester
✉ Top of Wellsway ☎ 832487
Spacious pub/restaurant. The dining area is completely separate with full grill menus and special children's meals. Children are welcome in pub area although requested to sit away from the bar. Carpeted toilets. No suitable outside area.

PUBS OUTSIDE BATH

SEE MAP ON PAGES 140/1
1. Bathampton Mill
✉ Mill Lane, Bathampton ☎ 469758
Spacious, friendly pub, lots of seating inside and out. Beefeater restaurant, also separate extensive bar menu. Highchairs in restaurant. Two play areas outside - one enclosed with swings and another unenclosed with more extensive play equipment. Plenty of toilet space. Reasonably-priced food with limited vegetarian choice. Access good. Popular so can get crowded in summer. Easy access to river and weir - keep a close eye on children.

2. Barge Inn
✉ Frome Road, Bradford-on-Avon ☎ 863403
Welcomes children anywhere in the pub and operates a children's menu. A large garden backing onto the canal (so watch toddlers). Lots of children's diversions, including garden chess and draughts with badminton and basketball facilities.

3. Canal Tavern
✉ 49 Frome Road, Bradford-on-Avon ☎ 865232
Children can go into the restaurant or main bar areas. Garden by the canal towpath with tables and caged birds. There are bar snacks and a restaurant menu, which caters for children. Honest pub grub. Access is easier with a buggy from the canal side. Watch for bikes and open water.

4. The Compton
✉ Court Hill, Compton Dando ☎ 01761 490321
Seating inside and out at this well-equipped pub. Small portions available. Swings in large grassy garden.

5. Cross Guns
✉ 160 Avoncliff ☎ 862335
Good selection of ales available at this picturesque pub. Separate room for families. Steep terraced garden above river. Picnic tables in garden and on level patio area. Good food, afternoon teas. Can get very crowded so arrive early for lunch. Parking is limited but possible to walk from Freshford, Limpley Stoke or Bradford-on-Avon. (See **Walks**) Nice train ride from Bath.

6. The Crown, Marshfield
✉ 16 High Street, Marshfield ☎ 891189
Children welcome inside and out. Children's menu available. Highly recommended Sunday lunches.

7. The Crown, Bathford
✉ Bathford Hill, Bathford ☎ 852297
A great kid's pub. Pleasant garden room, patio and large garden with sandpit and toys. Inside there is a selection of children's books. Full children's menu and highchairs provided. Sunday lunch time there's a Magician, all year round. Toilets have changing mat and baby wipes. Quite exceptional, one of our favourite pubs - but can get busy in summer, so its best to book, especially for Sundays.

8. The Crown, Saltford
✉ Bath Road, Saltford ☎ 872117
Children welcome outside in the lovely garden with swings, slides and climbing frame. Also animals, birds and ducks in enclosures. Benches and picnic tables. Bouncy castle and children's menu.

9. The Crown Inn, Dyrham
✉ Tolldown, Dyrham ☎ 891231
Lovely safe garden with good range of play

equipment. Eating space inside or out and children's menu throughout the year. Space to change a nappy in toilets.

10. Fleur de Lys
✉ Norton St Philip ☎ 01373 834333
Substantial Bar meals and children's menu. No garden, but alcoves where children can be reasonably contained. Good in winter as children welcomed in pub and dining room.

11. Fox and Badger
✉ The Square, Wellow ☎ 832293
Children are allowed in the main lounge if it's not busy (Sunday lunch is the busiest time). The restaurant area serves as a family room. Good-value homemade food. Children's menu and vegetarian selection. Book in advance for Sunday lunch and use of the highchair. You can get a single buggy through to the restaurant. (See **Walks**)

12. The George Inn, Norton St Philip
✉ High Street, Norton St Philip
☎ 01373 834224
One of the oldest pubs in Britain. Separate rooms available for families. No small portions but adult food suitable to share. Walled garden with a few steps to car-park. Playing field over the wall (access down alley on right of pub) with some play equipment.

13. The George Inn, Bathampton
✉ Mill Lane, Bathampton ☎ 425079
Child-friendly pub. Upstairs family room available in wet weather. Garden area fronts the canal – lots to look at. Toilets have changing mat. There is also a back garden with climbing frame and tables. Good food. Can be reached on foot from canal. (See **Walks**)

14. The Globe
✉ Newton St Loe ☎ 872649
Friendly pub that provides highchairs and a flexible children's menu. Interior has some steps but is basically safe.

15. Hop Pole
✉ Woods Hill, Limpley Stoke ☎ 723134
Enclosed garden to rear of the pub. Small games room (with dart board) that families can use for eating/drinking if they wish. 'Kiddies corner' menu: sausages, fishfingers, chips, etc.

16. Hope and Anchor
✉ Midford ☎ 832296
Pleasant country pub with food (some Spanish dishes). Children welcome inside or on patio area at rear. (See **Walks**)

17. Hunters Rest
✉ Clutton ☎ 01761 452303
Good playground with miniature train. Picnic tables. Separate children's room and menu (fishfingers, sausages, etc). A varied, good-quality adult menu. Plenty of space. Family Fun Night on Wednesdays during school summer holidays. Bristol Evening Post 'Family Pub of the Year 1994'.

18. The Inn at Freshford
✉ Freshford ☎ 722250
Attractive country pub. Separate dining room indoors. Very popular and crowded on Sundays (must book). Food is hearty and exceptionally good value. Pretty garden but slopes with some steep steps, so toddlers need watching. Pleasant walks possible around this pretty village. (See **Walks**)

19. Jolly Sailor
✉ Mead Lane, Saltford ☎ 873002
Lunches and bar snacks until 2.30pm. Teas and snacks at other times. Pretty views over the river, with sailing boats, ducks and a working lock. Garden next to the river. Picnic benches, some shade. Just off Bath/Bitton Cycleway so it's a good lunch spot for cyclists. Children allowed inside (probably best in the conservatory). Kid's portions available. A good food selection including vegetarian meals.

20. Longs Arms
✉ Upper South Wraxall (Between Box and Bradford-on-Avon) ☎ 864450
A pleasant garden with tables. Children's menu available. Family room with skittle alley at rear.

21. Northey Arms
✉ Ashley (near Box, on A4) ☎ 742333
A large pub with a lawned safe garden including play area, well away from the road. Children's menu. Picnic tables and a patio.

22. Old Station Inn
✉ Wells Road, Hallatrow ☎ 01761 452228
This village pub welcomes children. Space for

Pubs

families inside and out. A big back garden with swings and climbing frame. Children's menu.

23. Packhorse Inn
✉ Southstoke ☎ 832060
Lovely old pub which specialises in cider. A large garden on two levels, with swings. Good-quality, well-priced food and children's menu. (See **Walks**)

24. Red Lion
✉ Woolverton (on A36) ☎ 01373 830350
Popular with families as it is near Rode Bird Gardens. The pub and its grounds are safe for children with a suitable eating area. Children's menu available. Space to change a nappy in the toilets.

25. Ring O'Bells
✉ Compton Martin (on A368) ☎ 01761 221284
Garden with swings, slides, etc. Family room with toys and six highchairs! Children's menu. Varied, good-quality adult menu with some unusual dishes.

26. Riverside Bar
✉ St Margaret's Street, Bradford-on-Avon
☎ 863526
Children welcome inside, (Lego and Duplo to play with) and outside where there are picnic tables. Good after a dip at the swimming pool, which is close-by along the river path. Good variety of snacks. Children's portions available.

27. Slabhouse Inn
✉ Bath Road, (North of Wells) ☎ 01749 840310
Children's menu and small portions available at this family-run pub one mile north of Wells. Outside there is a garden with climbing frame, inside a family room.

28. The Swan Hotel
✉ Church Street, Bradford-on-Avon ☎ 868686
Families can eat in the bar or restaurant. Highchairs and kid's menu. Good food.

29. Vobster Inn
✉ Vobster, Near Mells, Somerset ☎ 01373 812920
Situated between Frome and Radstock on the edge of the Mendips. Hearty food with children's portions. Two play areas - one for pre-schoolers and one 'assault course' for older children.

30. Warwick Arms
✉ Upper Bristol Road, Clutton ☎ 01761 452256
Swings, slide, climbing frame, rocking toys and a wishing well. Picnic tables. Family area in the pub. Children's menu.

31. Wheatsheaf
✉ Combe Hay ☎ 833504
Exceptional food makes this a popular pub, so arrive early for lunch. Picturesque garden that has recently been landscaped into safe terraces – lots of space for children to run around. Barbecues on summer weekends. Lots of picnic tables. Room for buggies in the restaurant section but not in the rest of it. Children welcome, preferably not in the bar area but there are other rooms. No special kids' menu, but will split portions.

32. The White Hart, Ford
✉ Ford (on A420, near Castle Combe)
☎ 01249 782213
Children welcome in the restaurant or adjoining dining area everyday except Saturday nights. Good adult menu but no special children's menu (although sandwiches are available). Room for buggies unless very busy. There is a paved area outside with access to the road. Highchairs provided. Walks possible through woods to Castle Combe (not suitable for buggies).

33. The White Hart, Marshfield
✉ The Folly, Marshfield
☎ 891233
Families can use the large seating area inside the pub. Children's menu available. Spacious toilets. Two large areas of garden.

34. White Horse
✉ Biddestone, near Chippenham
☎ 01249 713305
Village pub with garden that has swings, slide, chipmunks, an aviary and rabbit enclosure. Children's portions available.

35. Ye Olde Kings Arms
✉ Litton (on B3114)
☎ 01761 241301
Large Mendip pub with separate area for children in the 'Old Kitchen' and the 'Armoury'. Highchairs and special children's menu available. Large gardens with swings, slides and picnic tables.

Safety

AvonSafe – Action for Safety in Bath and N.E. Somerset – is a multi-agency accident prevention group, comprising professionals from local authorities and health and emergency services, working together to improve safety and raise public awareness.

AvonSafe Contact Numbers

Road Safety
☎ 477127, Mike Baugh and Nick Brown. Road and in-car safety, cycle and pedestrian training.

Home and Water Safety, Environmental Health
☎ 477562, Helen Arnoldi

Police Community Affairs
☎ 842480, Sgt Mike Stanton. Crime prevention and Neighbourhood Watch, Vehicle Watch and SPLASH programme.

Avon Fire Brigade
☎ 0117 926 2061 x477, Steve Emery

Trading Standards
☎ 461293, Jeremy Parsons. Call if you have purchased anything you consider to be unsafe.

In-car Safety

The law states that car seat belts must be worn if fitted, and an appropriate child restraint (correct for the size and weight of your child) must be used. Child safety seats should be fitted correctly. Avoid second-hand car seats unless you are sure of the history. Seats which have suffered an impact are unlikely to be safe.

Walking

A huge increase in the use of the car for taking children to and from school has led to traffic chaos outside schools and has had a negative effect on road safety skills. Many children have little experience of crossing roads and so are more vulnerable when they become independent. Walking with your children, means you can teach them how to cross roads and to judge safe gaps in the traffic. It also keeps them fit without adding to Bath's traffic problems.

Cycling

Cycling is enjoyable and healthy, however there are some important safety issues to bear in mind. Children are most at risk when on the road without knowing how to ride correctly. They should know the Highway Code, what to expect from other road users and be able to spot and deal safely with potential hazards. Children over 10 can receive basic cycle safety training from the Traffic and Safety Team. Courses are sometimes organised by Primary schools. Younger children are unlikely to understand everything needed to cycle safely on their own. This is especially so for children who are normally ferried around by car.

Making cycling safer

If you drive a car yourself, remember to look out for bikes and slow down or stop if necessary. Give cyclists plenty of space and above all, be patient. Wearing a cycle helmet can reduce the risk of serious head injury under normal circumstances. It must be a good fit and fastened correctly. Make sure that the helmet doesn't interfere with vision.

Bath with your Kids

Safety

SAFETY IN THE HOME

The Home and Water Safety Officer

Environmental and Consumer Services Section, Trimbridge House, Bath ☎ 477000
Provide information, advice or training on all aspects of Safety and Accident prevention. Has a free resource library. Wide variety of accident prevention topics – leaflets, videos, books, posters, teaching packs etc. also catalogue available.

Home Safety Checklist

Under 5's are particularly at risk from accidents in the home.
Use the following list to see how safe your home is.

- Is there at least one working smoke alarm fitted in your home?
- Do you have a family fire escape plan and practice the family fire drill?
- Are heaters and fires in good working order with fire guards?
- Are matches and lighters kept well out of sight where children can't see or get at them?
- Are floors kept clear of clutter?
- Are electrical leads in good condition and positioned safely?
- Are electrical sockets overloaded?
- Are loose rugs secured?
- Are vases/liquid containers placed away from electrical items?
- Are chemicals and medicines stored in a secure place away from children?
- Is safety glass or safety film fitted on windows, doors and conservatories? (Use BS6206 A, B or C)
- Do bottles have child resistant caps?

Chemicals

Keep all potentially hazardous products well out of reach of children, preferably in a locked cupboard. This includes medicines and tablets, caustic or toxic chemicals such as dishwasher detergent, oven cleaner, bleach, antifreeze, garden products such as weed killers and pesticides. Make sure that you always buy bottles with child resistant caps. Dispose of all unwanted and out of date medicines – you can take them to a Chemist who will dispose of them for you. Always keep potentially hazardous products in original containers to avoid mistakes.

Toys

Most deaths caused by toys are due to choking on small parts, but the majority of injuries are caused by people falling over toys, or children falling off of toys. To help prevent accidents, buy the right toy for the right age - look for small parts and take note of warning notices. Check toys regularly and throw away if broken. Store safely and tidy up frequently. Look for toy safety marks – BS5665, the British Standards for Toys, The Lion Mark from the British Toy and Hobby Association and the CE Mark, for toys conforming to European Community Standard.

FOOD SAFETY

Environmental and Consumer Services

☎ 477000
Information on food labelling, weights, measures, food poisoning, allergies and all hygiene matters. Useful for prospective businesses or to take legal action on your behalf. Also for advice on food issues of public concern, like BSE.

Sanctuaries for Adults

Post Natal Exercise Classes

All sessions are run by Physiotherapists, and babies are welcome.

Manvers Street Baptist Church Hall
✉ Manvers Street
During term time, Friday 10.30-11.00am or 11.00am-12 noon. Gentler exercises for new mums after 6 week check.
Crèche run by WRVS volunteers at back of hall. Also an opportunity to meet other mothers for a cup of tea and a chat.

Bradford-on-Avon
✉ Health Centre ☎ 866611
Monday 11.00am-12 noon.

Trowbridge
✉ The Halve Clinic
☎ 766161
Thursday 11.00am-12 noon.

Chippenham
✉ Goldney Avenue Clinic
☎ 01249 653184
Monday 2.30am-4.00pm.

Frome
✉ The Health Centre
☎ 01373 464343
Tuesday 10.30am-12 noon.

Melksham
✉ Lowbourne Clinic
☎ 702443
Monday 2.00pm-3.30pm.

Devizes
✉ The Clinic, New Park Street
☎ 01380 722318
Thursday 1.30-3.00pm.

Fitness

Baskervilles School of Gymnastics
✉ Burnham Road, Lower Bristol Road, Bath
☎ 330001
Monday 9.30am, 12.30pm Aerobics, Tuesday 10.am Body Conditioning, 12.30pm Step and Tone, Thursday 10.00am Mum's Gymnastics 10.00am Beginners Step, Friday 9.30am Fab Abs (Fabulous Abdomens!) Crèche available, for maximum of 6 children. Cost £1 per child. Book in advance.

Bath Sports and Leisure Centre
✉ North Parade Road ☎ 462563
Squash, swimming, badminton, weights, keep-fit. Crèche available, weekdays 9.30am-12.30pm. £2.10 for the morning. Under 2's: 4 spaces, over 2's: 8. Book in advance in person.

Kickers
✉ Upper Bristol Road ☎ 461463
Crèche available Tuesday and Thursday 10.00-11.00am for aerobics or gym classes. Cost £1 per child age 6 weeks or over.

Combe Grove Manor Hotel and Country Club
✉ Shaft Road, Monkton Combe ☎ 835533
Fitness, indoor and outdoor swimming pools, gym, driving range, 5 hole golf course, squash, tennis and sauna. Crèche open 9.00am-1.00pm weekdays, 9.00am-3.00pm Saturday, 10.00am-2.00pm Sunday. Ages 4 weeks–7 years. Membership £655 per year plus a joining fee of £125. Children's membership for 0-4 years: £155, 5-15 years: £125.

Y Tots Day Nursery, International House
✉ Broad Street Place ☎ 460471
Sessions nursery for 18 months-5 years. Not directly linked to the Health Suite which operates gym and fitness classes, but will do drop-in sessions. £2.25 per hour.

Bath with your Kids

Sanctuaries for Adults

Adult Education

City of Bath College
✉ Avon Street
☎ 312191
Day nursery in Widcombe, for students and general public. Open Monday-Friday 8.30am-5.30pm. For up to 24 children, ages 18 months-5 years. Phone for a general prospectus. A range of women's education and training courses available, including Returner Programmes, Office Skills, Community Services.
There are some free and reduced rate courses for the unemployed. Crèche also free for some courses. Send for an Adult and Community Education prospectus.

University of Bath
✉ Claverton Down
☎ 826518
Westwood Day nursery open daily, all year round 8.45am-5.30pm, based on sessions for children 2-5 years.

The Womens Woodwork Centre
✉ Lambridge Mews, Larkhall ☎ 339482
Women and children's woodwork classes. Free places are available for unemployed women receiving benefit with financial help for child. (See **Activities and Clubs**)

Also see **Child care** and **Education**.

Chippenham College
✉ Cocklebury Road, Chippenham SN15 3QD
☎ 01249 444501
Pre-school available Monday-Friday 9.00am-3.15 or 4.15pm. Places available for children of students and staff.

Frome Community College
✉ Bath Road, Frome BA11 2HQ
☎ 01373 465353 Phone for a prospectus.
☎ 01373 453838 Little Oaks Nursery.
For students or general public. Open 50 weeks per year, 8.00am-4.45pm. Cost £7.75 per session.

Norton Radstock College
✉ South Hill Park, Radstock
☎ 01761 433161
Crèche available to students for maximum of 2 days, Monday-Friday, 9.00am-4.00pm. For children aged from 6 weeks.

And for full time students:
Longfellow Day Nursery
☎ 01761 410238
Monday-Friday 8.45am-5.15pm, 51 weeks per year, costs £7.00 per session.

Open University
✉ PO Box 72, Milton Keynes MK7 6AQ
☎ 01908 274066

Other

Bath Central Library
✉ The Podium, Northgate Street
☎ 428144
☎ 480110 for Children's Librarian
The children's library organises activities in the school holidays and has regular storytelling sessions during the week, giving parents half an hour free to browse. Under 5's story time, Tuesday 2.15-2.45pm, over 4's story time Saturday 11-11.30am.

Bath Centre for Voluntary Service
✉ 3 Abbey Green ☎ 464015
Link service between voluntary groups and the statutory sector. Opening hours: Monday-Thursday 9.30am-4.30pm. Offers help for those setting up Community Groups.
If you would like to help others there is also a Volunteer Bureau, open Tuesday-Thursday, 10.00am-12.30pm and 1.00-3.30pm, ☎ 465125.

Recreation

Woolley Grange
✉ Woolley Green, Bradford-on-Avon
☎ 864705
Eat in peace while your children are looked after in the on-site crèche, 10am-6pm. Book in advance. See **Eating Out**.

The Old Bell
✉ Malmesbury ☎ 01666 822344
Enjoy a peaceful meal while children go to the on-site crèche, 10am-6pm and playground. Book in advance. See **Eating Out**.

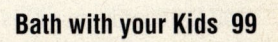

Shops

We have tried to list as many of the shops that you may have to visit for and with your children. Our aim is practical, indicating ease of access and manoeuvrability, the range of goods sold and what, if any, facilities there are.

Unless otherwise stated, shops say they will let a child use their staff loo in an emergency. Opening hours are mostly 9am-5.30pm, but many shops now stay open until 7 or 8pm.

When buying toys look for the CE mark which means they have been rigorously tested and have passed the safety standards of both the EEC and the British Standards Institute. Another safety symbol, the Lion Mark, has been introduced by some major toy manufacturers and means the toy has passed the British Standards Institute tests.

Any complaints about the standard of goods should be made to the shop concerned. If you are not satisfied with their response you may find it helpful to contact Citizens' Advice Bureau on 463333 or Trading Standards on 461293

BABY EQUIPMENT

For Sale:

Argos (see *Toy Shops*)
Co-op (see *Clothes*)
Early Learning Centre (see *Further Afield*)
The Golden Cot (see *Toy Shops*)
John Lewis (see *Further Afield*)
Mothercare (see *Clothes*)

For Hire:

Nursery Thyme (see *Further Afield*)

BOOK SHOPS

County Bookshops

✉ 3 Burton Street ☎ 424006
✉ Marchant's Passage
☎ 469659

Discount bookshop, including children's books. Further discounts for parties and schools. Rather cramped - buggies difficult.

Good Buy Books

✉ 6 North Parade ☎ 469625

Bargain book shop with wide range of titles at half price or less, with children's section. Limited space for buggy, friendly staff. Open late, about 8pm.

Pumpkin Books

✉ The Podium, Northgate Street ☎ 335121

Small selection of quality discount books for children. Spacious shop with easy access.

SPCK Bookshops

✉ 3 Forum Buildings (opposite back entrance to McDonalds) ☎ 466092

Christian bookshops with children's books, prayer books, bibles, tapes and 'knick-knacks'. Easy access, but children's section upstairs. SPCK music shop two doors along.

Waterstones

✉ 4 Milsom Street
☎ 448515
☎ 448595 Mail Order

Large book store with extensive range of general

Bath with your Kids 99

Shops

and specialised books. Wonderful children's section on ground floor at back of store with books suitable for all ages and some tapes. Cuddly toys to play with and seats for browsers. Narrow aisles to negotiate, just possible with double buggy if you are determined. Cafe and loo on first floor. No lift.

Whitemans Bookshop

✉ 7 Orange Grove ☎ 464029
General bookshop with good quality and quite sizeable children's section on ground floor. Helpful staff with good advice on choosing suitable books. Just space for a single buggy. Will find space for breast feeding if asked and let desperate toddlers use staff loo.

W.H.Smith

✉ Union Street ☎ 460522
Children's books upstairs with small chairs, table and a video showing. Lift at back of store which will take a double buggy. Disabled loo for customers.

CHARITY SHOPS

Barnardo's

✉ 30 Shaftesbury Road ☎ 330339
Second hand clothes with a reasonable range of children and baby clothes; also some books and toys. Has a small play table with toys to keep your children occupied while you browse. Two steps at entrance, inside there is room for a single buggy. Public loos can be found across the road, near the bottle bank. Some parking around Moorlands Road.

Dorothy House Shop

✉ 30 Westgate Buildings ☎ 482606
✉ 15 Moorland Road ☎ 444695
Sells second-hand children's clothes, toys and books. Roomy, with level access. Open Monday-Saturday 9.30am-4.30pm.

Oxfam

✉ Argyle Street ☎ 466798
Cards, gifts, books and kids equipment on ground floor, and adult and children's clothes on first floor all at very reasonable prices in aid of charity. Only sells toys that carry a `CE' mark. Access wide enough for buggy but some steps. Open: Monday-Saturday 9.30am-4.30pm.

Oxfam

✉ 12 George Street ☎ 464838
Same goods as above. Awkward access for a buggy, but all on the ground floor.

Save the Children

✉ 7 Walcot Street ☎ 447236
Sells clothes, books, cards and gifts at cheap prices for their charity. All toys bear a CE mark. Tight squeeze for a double buggy. Opening hours Monday-Saturday 10am-4pm.

Shaw Trust

✉ 11 George Street ☎ 460225
Charity shop selling cards, gifts and second hand clothes, books and bits and pieces. Easy access Also at 36 Moorland Road, Oldfield Park.

CLOTHES – CHILDREN AND MATERNITY

Adams

✉ 7 Southgate ☎ 463800
Complete range of reasonably priced children clothes from 0-9 year-olds. Automatic doors and room for a double buggy. Have their own child friendly loos.

Benetton

✉ 26 High Street ☎ 462466
Bright and attractive clothes for 0-12 year olds, including coats, trousers and shirts, as well as adult garments. Good quality but not cheap. Room for single buggy.

Boots

✉ 1 Merchant's Passage, Southgate ☎ 464402
Children's clothes and toys as well as Chemist. All nappy requirements, children's crockery, baby food and toiletries. Also sells pregnancy and nursing bras and maternity swimwear. Baby changing and feeding rooms with nappies, tissues, bottle-warmer and a potty (but where to empty potty is a problem). Management policy allows customers to use staff loos. Automatic door, aisles can get crowded for double buggy.

British Home Stores

✉ 2 Southgate ☎ 423527
Children's clothes on ground floor. Easy access Plenty of space for buggies. Loos with enough space to change a baby.

100 Bath with your Kids

Shops

C & A
✉ 23 High Street ☎ 463288
Clothing store for all ages, plus accessories. Good, cheap clothes. Can use Staff toilets. Easy access for buggies.

C.R.S. (Co-op)
✉ Westgate Buildings ☎ 463811
Boys and girls clothes: birth to 7/8 years. Also baby equipment and toys at competitive prices. Children's department upstairs via customer lift. No changing facilities.

Dorothy Perkins
✉ 24 Stall Street ☎ 448547
Selection of maternity clothes including swimwear upstairs. Customer lift.

Gap Kids
✉ 17 Milsom Street ☎ 483822
Stylish clothes for up to 13/14 years plus shoes and hats. Not cheap but sales have healthy reductions. Spacious and airy with easy access. Can breastfeed in changing room.

Golden Cot
Continental clothing (See listing under *Toys*).

Just Kids
✉ 19 Northumberland Place ☎ 464389
Clothes from birth to about 15 years, small selection of footwear. Limited space so a bit awkward with a buggy. Interesting and unusual selection of stylish continental clothing.

Laura Ashley
✉ New Bond Street ☎ 460341
Lovely girls' clothes from 6 months to 9 years as well as adult clothes. Not cheap. Children's section on ground floor. Helpful staff.

Littlewoods
✉ Stall Street ☎ 465818
Department store selling range of children's clothing plus school uniforms. Children's section upstairs, double buggy fits in lift. Baby changing facilities in disabled and ladies loos. Cafe. Easy access with a buggy.

Marks & Spencer
✉ 16 Stall Street ☎ 462591
Good quality clothes. Children's section, toilets and baby changing facilities on second floor. Two large (but busy) customer lifts. Also sells food and furnishings. Easy access with automatic door at front entrance.

Monsoon
✉ 1 Upper Borough Walls ☎ 463500
Interesting but pricey girls' clothes in typical 'Monsoon' style. 2-10 years old.

Mothercare
✉ 42-48 Southgate ☎ 466425
Children's clothes from 0-10 years-olds and range of maternity wear. Toys for up to fives. Nursery and baby equipment. Baby changing room for use by Mums and Dads. Spacious shop, easy access, room for double buggy.

Next
✉ 16-17 Union Street ☎ 469828.
Children's section for 0-13 year olds with exciting and attractive clothes and shoes. Good quality, but not cheap. Mail order available. Also children's bed linen, wall paper etc. Changing rooms downstairs.

Principles
✉ 35-36 Stall Street ☎ 446519
Children's section for 0-8 year olds, both boys and girls. Good selection, but upstairs with no lift.

Roundabout
✉ Prior Park Road, Widcombe ☎ 316696
Designer, sample and second-hand children's clothes from 0-12 years. Some toys, and baby equipment for sale or hire. Easy access. Convenient on-street parking. Open Monday-Saturday 9.30am-5pm.

Scholars
✉ Terrace Walk ☎ 462206
Small shop selling basic school clothing, including uniforms for Bath schools, and some sports gear for children and adults including sports holdalls.

Stock Exchange
✉ 20 Moorland Road, Oldfield Park ☎ 444744
Nearly new women's, teens and children's clothes. Easy access. Open Monday-Saturday 9.15am-4.45pm.

Tammy
✉ 10 The Mall, Southgate ☎ 330126
Complete range of girls clothes for ages 6-14, from

Bath with your Kids

Shops

underwear to overcoats, from smart to casual, including accessories. Limited space for buggies. Loo in café opposite.

Tumi
✉ 8/9 New Bond Street ☎ 446025
Latin American products: mobiles, toys, music, to name a few, plus small selection of jumpers, cotton dungarees and hats. Adults and children 6 months-12 years.

Whoops
✉ Moorlands Road, Oldfield Park ☎ 426814
Seconds clothes, overmakes, wrong sizes and rejects - at reduced prices, with a children's section. Bargains to be had. One step at entrance, small shop but room for a single buggy. Street parking.

Woolworths
✉ 54, Moorland Road, Oldfield Park ☎ 424715
Small branch of national chain selling Ladybird clothes, toys, stationery, videos, some computer games, etc. Wide doors. Public loos nearby. Worth a trip.

HOBBY SHOPS

Bath Stamp and Coin Shop
✉ 12 Pulteney Bridge ☎ 463073
Enthusiasts shop for stamp and coin collecting with starter kits for beginners, albums, bags of coins and collectors' guides. Small shop, step at entrance.

Bath Model Centre
✉ 2 Lower Borough Walls ☎ 460115
Models of tanks, trains, boats, cars, planes to make, as well as jewellery kits and Disney kits. Plus all necessary materials including paints, batteries and equipment. Also radio controlled models and ready-made toys. Confined space and 2 steps up to shop so not suitable for buggies. Toddlers would need to be supervised. Nearby public loos.

Craft Technique
✉ 19 Old Orchard Street ☎ 465717
Sells a variety of crafts: beads, rug-making, needlepoint and embroidery kits and equipment, dying materials, toy kits, raffia, fabric paints, jewellery kits and those elusive fiddly items like eyes for soft toys or shoe buckles. Buggies best left at door. Toddlers need to be watched as lots of reachable fascinating articles. In a quiet side street reached from Pierrepont Street or New Orchard Street. Closed Mondays.

F. J. Harris and Son
✉ 13/14 Green Street ☎ 462116
Artists' materials shop and picture framers. For children there is Fimo, beginners' painting sets, fabric paints, poster paints, brushes, crayons, pencils and books. Steep step down and narrow door. Narrow inside.

Minerva Graphics
✉ 12a Trim Street ☎ 464054
Art equipment for all ages and ability, including technical equipment. For children there are oil pastels, sugar paper, poster paints, beginners' painting kits, coloured pencils and easels. Two steps at Trim Street entrance, split level shop.

Stamps
✉ 3 North Parade Passage ☎ 465492
Stamps, albums and accessories. Also model cars and albums for postcards and coins. Wonderful shop for enthusiasts. Upstairs - very difficult with a buggy. Open Monday, Wednesday-Friday 1.30-4.30pm, Saturday 9.30-11.30am and 1.30-4.30pm.

MARKETS

Eastville Market
✉ Bristol M32 Junction 2
Open Friday and Sunday. Huge – a proper market! Sells almost everything.

Green Park Station
Open Monday-Saturday. Stalls vary daily: Crafts, clothes, wools, hand-made knits toys, discount books, etc.

Guildhall Market
Open Monday-Saturday, shop hours but some stalls close at 4pm. Fresh fruit, flowers and vegetables. Meat, specialist cheese stall and delicatessen. Second-hand books. Haberdashery, sheepskins, bags, hardware stalls, and more. Well worth a browse.

Shops

Odd Down Football Club
✉ Odd Down, next to St. Gregory's School Open Saturday. Stalls as for Twerton.

Twerton Market
✉ Bath City Football Ground, behind Twerton High Street
Thursdays 9am-12pm. Sells almost everything; fish, vegetables, fruit, meat, clothes, household items, plants, pet supplies, etc. Good for buggies.

Walcot Flea Market
✉ Old SWEB building, Walcot Street
Open at weekends for antiques, clothes and bric-a-brac.

Music Shops

Bath Music Centre
✉ 20 Monmouth Place ☎ 335154
Large range of sheet music, and a variety of instruments. Offer instrument loan service, where you hire instrument to see if your child likes it before you buy. Child must be having lessons at school.

Duck, Son & Pinker
✉ 1/2 Pulteney Bridge ☎ 465975
Music shop with 3 outlets including Milsoms. Specialises in pianos and keyboards of all types. Just negotiable with a buggy. Large items are delivered.

Duck, Son & Pinker
✉ 9 Bridge Street (next to Pulteney Bridge shop) ☎ 465975
Sells instruments for all ages. Including recorders, flutes, violins and guitars. Arrange repairs for some woodwind and string instruments. Good and practical trial scheme of instruments for school children.

C. Milsom and Son
✉ 12 Northgate Street ☎ 465975
Large range of sheet music, teaching guides, exam music and books for all ages and levels of ability, both popular and classical. Also CDs, records, cassettes and videos. Split level store. Easy access. Part of Duck, Son and Pinker Ltd.

Party Items and Cakes

Bryans Toys
See *Toy Shops*.

Cooper Hardware
✉ 91 Bradford Road, Combe Down ☎ 833675
All you need for cake making: boards, decorations, candles and equipment. Can hire tins by the day in various novelty shapes. General hardware store with some gardening equipment. Easy parking. Limited space inside.

Kitchens
✉ 4 Quiet Street ☎ 330524
Everything to do with cakes: ribbons, candles, decorations, icing equipment, variety of cake tins including novelty shapes. Easy access.

The following shops will make cakes of various shapes and designs for special occasions. They usually need a couple of weeks notice:

Waitrose
✉ The Podium, Northgate Street ☎ 442550

Taste Buds
✉ 12 Bartlett Street (between top of Milsom Street and Assembly Rooms) ☎ 480139

Mountstevens
✉ 1 Lower Borough Walls ☎ 400267 (also shops in Moorland Road, Bathwick and Bear Flat).

Shoe Shops

Clarks
✉ 1/2 Union Street ☎ 462632
Sells all types of shoes, including slippers, wellies and trainers. Children's department downstairs, no lift but helpful staff will carry or mind your buggy. Trained shoe fitters. Guarantee to uphold standards of Children's Foot Health Register. Play area with Duplo bricks.

Hush Puppies
✉ 34 Stall Street ☎ 460424
Own brand only. Children's department on ground floor. Helpful staff and toys. Fitting service measuring width, depth and length of feet. Depth and width of each foot fitted

Bath with your Kids

Shops

separately - useful if your child's feet are different. Fit is guaranteed, and will change if shoes don't fit properly.

Jones
✉ 19 Cheap Street ☎ 465617
Children's department upstairs, staff will mind your buggy or help carry it upstairs. Brands include Clarks, Startrite, Ritcher and Naf Naf. Trained shoe fitters. Guarantee to uphold standards of Children's Foot Health Register. Rocking horse to divert children.

Russell and Bromley
✉ 16-17 Old Bond Street ☎ 460951
Good range of shoes including Clarks, Startrite, R&B and designer shoes. Children's department in basement, access by stairs only. Has play area. Will measure feet and spend time fitting. Staff helpful, will help carry or watch buggies. Guarantee to uphold standards of Children's Foot Health Register. Spacious with easy access.

If you're going near Street in Somerset, it's worth a detour to buy from the discount shoe shops which line the main shopping street, selling end-of-ranges and seconds stock from the nearby shoe factories.

SPORTS, BIKE AND DANCEWEAR SHOPS

Allsports
✉ 4 Southgate ☎ 425998
Sells sports clothing, footwear and sports equipment ranging from rackets to exercise machines. Easy access but narrow gangways.

Aqua Leisure
✉ Abbeygate Street ☎ 446681
In winter sells ski products: ski clothes and accessories from about age 2 upwards, with skis and other hardware from about 7 up. In summer sells swimwear, wetsuits, floats and watersports equipment. Large equipment upstairs. No lift. Easy access.

Avon Valley Cyclery
✉ Rear of Bath Railway Station ☎ 461880
Lots of bikes for hire, including children's bikes,

Clarks

Made in Bath, Sold in Bath

Over 170 Years of Fitting Shoes for Growing Feet

The Clarks Shop, 1-2 Union Street
BATH BA1 1RP - 01225 462632

Shops

baby seats and helmets and wide range of bikes and equipment for sale. Also do repairs.

I M Crudgington Ltd.
✉ 37 Broad Street ☎ 464928
Specialist fishing and gun shop with children's fishing equipment. Also sells country clothes for adults. On two floors, limited space but room for a buggy. Closed Monday.

J.C. Hare Ltd.
✉ 30 Moorland Road, Oldfield Park ☎ 422674
Bike shop and Raleigh dealer; traditional bikes from toddler trikes upwards to mountain bikes. Sells spares and all bike equipment like child's seats, safety helmets, locks, lights etc. Toddlers will need watching as plenty of enticing goods at hand reach. Parking for one hour in front of shop. Closed for lunch 1-2pm weekdays.

Intersport
✉ 9 The Mall, Southgate ☎ 462421
Sells children's sports clothing and footwear from size 5. Easy access for buggies.

John's Bikes
✉ 82 Walcot Street ☎ 334633
Specialist shop with range of bikes for children. Free service one month after purchase. Also sell safety helmets and baby seats. Limited on-street parking. Access OK for buggy; staff will help with double buggy.

John Moore Sports Ltd.
✉ 13 Argyle Street ☎ 466341
Sports' shop which has some child-sized games equipment, e.g. for tennis, squash, cricket and hockey. Also swimwear (upstairs) and trainers from size 1 upwards. A couple of steps at entrance.

Karan Lesley
✉ Green Park Station ☎ 319164
Official R.A.D. ballet clothes including tutus. Dance shoes including point, ballroom and tap shoes. Also majorette outfits; adult leisure clothes for keep fit etc. and ballet related gifts and novelties. Plenty of space. Loo nearby in Green Park. Also holds dance classes - Widcombe, Larkhall and City Centre, call for details and see **Activities and Clubs**.

Olympus Sports
✉ 20 Union Street ☎ 462039
Sports clothing, equipment and footwear. Very cramped shop. Not easily accessible with a buggy and on two floors without a lift.

Park Sports
✉ Faulkland Road, Oldfield Park ☎ 444789
General sports shop selling clothes, trainers, footballs etc. Doesn't have a vast range of equipment. It's a small shop, negotiable with single buggy, with one step at the entrance. Check opening times as very flexible!

Sportshoe
✉ 92 Walcot Street ☎ 460509
Sports shoes from size 5. Good access for buggy. Also has mail order.

Terry Warner Sports Ltd.
✉ 13 Westgate Street ☎ 461996
Sells footwear and clothing for children. Also mini sports equipment e.g. small tennis rackets. Easy buggy access.

Toy Shops

Air Circus
✉ 18 Northumberland Place ☎ 444512
Kite and juggling shop for children and adults. Large stock of sports kites and kite accessories, also spinning plates and unicycles. Mail order catalogue. In alley off the High Street.

Argos
✉ 3 Merchant's Passage, Southgate ☎ 462762
Catalogue Shopping with competitively priced children's toys and baby equipment. Can collect by car up above shop.

Bears in the Wood
✉ Unit 5, Shires Yard, Milsom Street ☎ 445880
Tuesday-Saturday 9.30am-5pm. Wonderful selection of bears and accessories from approx. £1 upwards. Access from Broad Street. Worth a look for bear lovers!

Boggle Juggling Shop
✉ 9 Broad Street ☎ 446685
Juggling equipment and books, also stocks magic

Bath with your Kids 105

Shops

products, unicycles, pedal-goes, batons, frisbees, jester hats and some stocking fillers. Bright and spacious shop with practice room. Mail order catalogue. Friendly, accommodating staff, will find you a place to breast feed if needs be. Open Monday-Saturday 10am-6pm.

Boots
✉ 1 Merchant's Passage, Southgate ☎ 464402
Brightly coloured baby toys, 'role play' toys, puzzles, art materials, sticker books etc.

Bryan's Toys
✉ 34 Wellsway, Bear Flat ☎ 427274
Wide range of toys, good selection of party neccesities and novelties such as hats, balloons, stocking fillers, party bags as well as plates and tablecloths. Also Ladybird books, colouring books, presents, cards etc. Limited space and lots for toddlers to fiddle with. Convenient street parking. Closed for lunch from 1-2.15pm.

Disney Store
✉ 9 Union Street ☎ 429853
Selling all things Disney including videos, cassette tapes, clothes, cuddly animals, Mickey Mouse ears, fancy dress, stationery etc. Good place for presents. Life-sized video screen constantly playing and moving mechanical models to keep the children occupied. No loos. Spacious. Open Monday-Saturday 9am-6pm.

Early Learning Centre
✉ Cheap Street ☎ 466321
Large range of educational toys and books. Also sells larger toys and play equipment, like playhouses, climbing frames and paddling pools. Lovely play area allowing parents to look around freely. Organised play time from 10am-12pm once a week. Catalogue. Buggy negotiable. Baby room. For baby equipment and children's clothes also at The Galleries, Broadmead, Bristol ☎ 0117 926 8645.

The English Teddy Bear Co.
✉ Abbey Church Yard ☎ 338655
Open Monday-Saturday 10am-6pm. Stocks teddies and T-shirts with teddy motifs plus a small selection of children's clothes.

The Golden Cot
✉ 2 Abbeygate Street ☎ 463739/464914
All sorts of toys for all ages, including models (to make and radio controlled), computer games, soft toys, the wherewithal for painting, drawing, outdoor equipment, and tricycles. Also, nursery and baby equipment, prams and buggies. Continental baby and children's clothes. Access easy with double buggy. Prams etc. upstairs, no lift. Buggies will be watched. Loos and baby-changing facilities.

John Menzies
✉ 2 Merchant's Passage, Southgate ☎ 460905
Toys, games, records and videos upstairs, no lift. Stationery and art materials downstairs.

Once a Tree Ltd.
✉ 5 Saracen Street ☎ 442680
Toys and gifts made from wood - boats, games, mobiles, clocks, traditional toys etc.

Paddington and Friends
✉ 1 Abbey Street ☎ 463598
Wide range of toys, gifts and books featuring Paddington Bear, Winnie the Pooh, Thomas the Tank Engine, Rupert Bear and other favourite characters. (Shop owned by Michael Bond, the creator of Paddington.) Two steps at entrance, room for a single buggy – just. Open Monday-Saturday 9.30am-6pm.

Tridias
✉ 124 Walcot Street ☎ 314730
A children's heaven selling toys of all shapes and sizes to suit all tastes, ages and pockets; from party-bags and stocking-fillers to huge dolls houses and forts, including teddies, trains, ride-ons, games and books. Stocks Brio, Galt and other reputable brands. Well worth a visit if you're in the area. Mail order catalogue. Children's play area, a long way from the door. Helpful staff. Children's loo and room to change and feed babies. Large spacious shop, with easy access.

Woolworths
✉ 54, Moorland Road, Oldfield Park ☎ 424715
See *Clothes Shops*.

WORTH KNOWING ABOUT

Bath Doll's Hospital
✉ 2 Grosvenor Place ☎ 319668
Modern and antique doll casualties treated at the Doll's Hospital by prior appointment.

Shops

'Dr' Mark See-Evans is a member of the Guild of Master Craftsmen for mending dolls, one of only two such people in the country.

Body Shop
✉ 2B Burton Street ☎ 446332
Environmentally-friendly and cruelty-free toiletries, including baby range. Return bottles to be recycled - discount offered. Children love the novelty soaps.

The Green Store
✉ 9 Green Street ☎ 427155
Environmentally sound products including reusable nappies, unbleached cotton underwear, T-shirts, some adult clothes, toiletries, stationery and educational activities and games.

Harvest
✉ 37 Walcot Street ☎ 465519
Independent wholefood shop. Wide range of wholefood and organic produce: wine, dairy, sugar and wheat free products. Cookery books for special diets. Wonderful bread and Deli. Homeopathic and Bach Flower remedies. Large well-stocked play-pen. Best noticeboard in town. Spacious, easy access for double buggy.

Homebase
✉ Green Park Station, Pinesway ☎ 339225
DIY chain store. Sells baby safety locks and equipment, paddling pools, sledges etc. as well as tool hire, DIY goods and everything for gardens. Toddlers need watching - lots of tools to 'investigate'. Automatic doors, ramps and wide aisles. Free parking for 2 hours. Spacious disabled loo with enough room to change a baby. Small ladies loo. Opening hours: Monday-Friday 8.30am-8pm, Saturday 8am-7pm, Sunday 9am-6pm.

Sainsburys
✉ Green Park Station, Pinesway ☎ 444737
Easy access with automatic doors, ramps and wide aisles but does get very crowded. A few parent and child parking slots near entrance and variety of specialised trolleys. Loos and feeding and changing room situated about 100 yards from store, bit basic, will fit a trolley but not well sign-posted. Staff will help pack bags, and carry shopping to car. Free phone for taxis in main entrance. 2 hours free parking - have to queue for entry at peak times. Late night and Sunday opening.

Stone the Crows
✉ 3 Broad Street ☎ 460231
Stocking fillers, card, wrapping paper. Mainly upstairs, so difficult with a buggy, but worth checking out especially at Christmas.

Waitrose
✉ The Podium, Northgate Street ☎ 442550
Supermarket with wide aisles, automatic doors, easy access for double buggy. Helpful staff. Easy but expensive parking nearby. Use Podium Card (application available from Podium Shops) for 1 hour free parking Monday-Thursday. Free parking Thursday evening and Sunday. Loos in Podium but staff will take desperate toddlers to staff loos in an emergency. Late night opening most nights. Open Sundays 11am-5pm.

---

for a washable nappy system that really works! and wonderfully soft organic cotton babywear

phone for our catalogue

the green store

Bath 404080

Shops

Further Afield

Bishopston Trading Company
✉ 33 Silver Street, Bradford-on-Avon ☎ 867485
Attractive, reasonably-priced, cotton clothes for all ages. Also jewellery, bolts of cotton, Indian dolls, quilted bags, gifts etc. Play area. Can breast feed in changing room. Just negotiable with a buggy. Worker's co-operative creating employment in the south Indian village of K. V. Kuppam where goods are made.
Also at 193 Gloucester Road, Bishopston, Bristol ☎ 0117 9245598.

Children's World
✉ Eastgate Centre, Eastville, Bristol (M32, Junction 2, near Tescos) ☎ 0117 951 8200
Wide range of clothes, equipment and toys etc. for 0-12's. Children's hairdresser. Under 7's soft play area with video and slide. Restaurant with kids' menu. Loos, changing and feeding rooms. Free parking, but gets busy at weekends. Bus 4 or 5 from Bristol city centre. Monday-Friday 10am-8pm, Saturday 9am-6pm, Sunday 10am-5pm.

Georges
✉ Atlas Street, Bristol ☎ 0117 971 6376
A gold-mine for cheap and cheerful goods ideal for stocking fillers, party bags, prizes, lucky dips. Also paper tablecloths, stationery, soft toys, games, and more. Open Monday-Friday 9am-5pm. Close Temple Meads Station.

John Lewis
✉ 1 The Horsefair, Broadmead, Bristol
☎ 0117 927 9100
Closed Sunday/Monday. Open late Thursday. Large store, excellent baby equipment, kids' clothes and toys. Also maternity wear. Soon to move to Cribbs Causeway (Junction 17 on M5).

Nursery Thyme
✉ Wharfside, Couch Lane, Devizes
☎ 01380 721747
Sells good quality new and used baby equipment. Has a part-exchange scheme. Hires out baby equipment. Mail order catalogue.

People and Planet
✉ Island House, Swineford Mill, Swineford, near Bitton ☎ 0117 323505
Shop in converted barn, sells fascinating range of products from developing countries - crafts, toys, jewellery and bags. Also recycled paper products. Café, see **Eating Out**. Open April-December, Wednesday-Saturday 10.30am-5pm.

Rainbows
✉ 80 High Street, Midsomer Norton
☎ 01761 412238
Well-stocked independent toy shop. Radio-controlled cars, models, scalextric, dolls, train sets, scooters and toys and games. Lego table to keep kids happy. Staircase to showroom. Also at 40, The High Street, Keynsham. 0117 986 8311.

Toys 'R' Us
✉ Cribbs Causeway, Centurion's Lane, Patchway, Bristol ☎ 0117 9591430
Huge range of all types of toys. Also clothes for 0-4 years. Baby changing in loos. Free parking. Accessible from Junction 17 on M5. Open Monday-Thursday and Saturday 9am-8pm, Friday 9am-9pm, Sunday 10am-6pm.

BISHOPSTON TRADING COMPANY

Beautiful clothes for Women & Children
Fair Trading & Fair Prices
Natural Fabric & Glorious colours
English Design & Indian Craftsmanship

RING 0117 924 5598
FOR MAIL ORDER CATALOGUE

33 SILVER STREET
BRADFORD-ON-AVON
and in Bristol, Stroud, Totnes & Glastonbury

A Workers' Co-operative set up to create employment in South India.

Swimming Pools and Sports Centres

This section provides information on Aquanatal, Parent and Baby and Family Swimming sessions. For swimming lessons, see Activities and Clubs. Your child should wear a swimming costume or cotton pants. Nappies and plastic pants soon become waterlogged and uncomfortable.

SWIMMING POOLS

Bath Sports and Leisure Centre

✉ North Parade Road, Bath ☎ 462563/5

Two chlorinated pools. Recently refurbished. 25m pool and a leisure pool with flume, river ride and water cannons. Also bubble jets, a play pool and dolphin slide. Both pools used by schools, clubs and for courses. Crèche: Monday-Friday 9.30am-12.30pm, for children 8 weeks to 5 years. Places limited (4 spaces for under 2's, 8 spaces for over 2's) so book as early as you can because it's popular! Bookings are taken up to eight days in advance, but you need to go in person unless you are a member of the centre, in which case you can book by phone. You must stay in the building while using the crèche. Changing rooms are single sex, with play-pen/nappy changing facilities in the ladies. Three family changing rooms – very busy at peak times. Children under 9 must be accompanied by an adult. Family Swimming: Saturday 2-5pm, Sunday 8am-5pm. Parent and Baby: Monday 9am-12.30pm, Wednesday 12.30-2pm, 2.30-4pm, Friday 11.30am-1.30pm. Note! Only one parent per child. 10 week courses available for toddlers including Gym and Swim and Water babies Watertots. Changing areas can be cold.

Bradford Pool

✉ St.Margaret's Street, Bradford-on-Avon
☎ 862970

Main and small pool, both chlorinated. No crèche. Pleasant changing rooms which are single sex with play-pen and nappy changing facilities. Parents and Toddlers: (under 5's) Monday 10-11 am, Tuesday 10-11.15 am, Wednesday 2-3.30pm Thursday 10.30 am-12 noon. Fun Session: (play rafts, inflatables, pool toys) Saturday 10.30 am-12 noon and 1-2.30 pm, Sunday 1-2.30 pm. Aqua Bump and Bump Away: (gentle exercise for mums-to-be and new mums with a swim afterwards) Tuesday 6.30-7.30 pm. Pools warm, facilities clean and staff helpful.

Clarendon Sports Centre

✉ Frome Road, Trowbridge ☎ 764342

One main pool, chlorinated. Single sex changing rooms. No crèche. Parent and Toddler: Monday 10-11am. Aquanatal: 2.45-3.45pm (gentle exercise for mums-to-be from 16 weeks onwards).

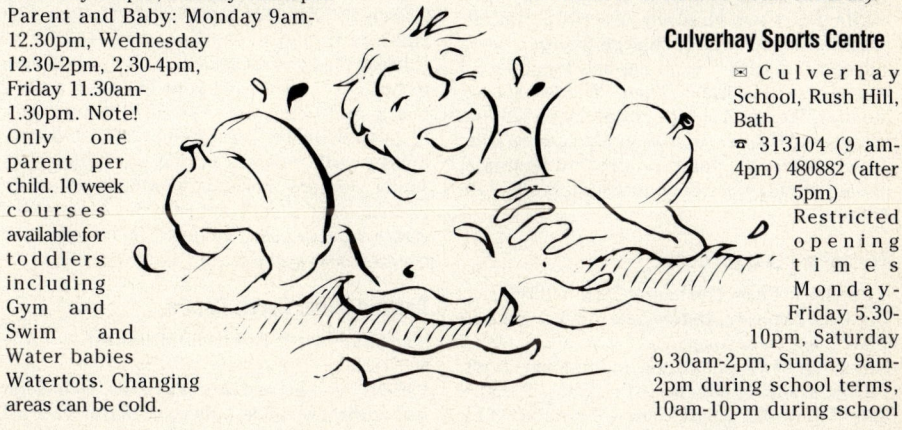

Culverhay Sports Centre

✉ Culverhay School, Rush Hill, Bath
☎ 313104 (9 am-4pm) 480882 (after 5pm)

Restricted opening times Monday-Friday 5.30-10pm, Saturday 9.30am-2pm, Sunday 9am-2pm during school terms, 10am-10pm during school

Bath with your Kids 109

Swimming Pools and Sports Centres

holidays. One 22m pool, single sex changing rooms with no baby facilities. No crèche available. Kids Fun-Time: Monday 6-7pm. Happy Hour (with inflatables): Saturday 1-2pm Swimming courses (beginners upwards, adult and children's sessions) Monday, Wednesday, Friday, Saturday.

Frome Leisure Centre

✉ Princess Anne Road, Frome ☎ 01373 465445
Two pools, both chlorinated. Main 25m pool plus small pool with steps for playing at the shallow end. Opening times vary between college holidays and term time. Single sex changing rooms with play-pens. Children under 8 must be accompanied by an adult. No crèche. Water Babes: Sunday 8.30-9.00am, Tuesday and Friday 3.30-4.00pm. 10 week swimming courses available for toddlers.

Keynsham Leisure Centre

✉ Temple Street, Keynsham ☎ 0117 986 1274
One main 25m pool, chlorinated. Single sex changing rooms with play-pens. Stairs down into changing rooms. Crèche. Thursday 10.00am-12.00 noon. Water Babies: Thursday 11.30am-12.30pm, 'Frolic' Fun Swim: Fridays 5.30-6.30pm.

The Olympiad Leisure Centre

✉ Monkton Park, Chippenham ☎ 01249 444144
One main ozonated pool with two flumes, jacuzzi, water jets, water cannon and rapid ride. There is a shallow area for non-swimmers but the current pull from the rapids is quite strong. Used by schools, clubs and for classes. Children under 8 years must be accompanied by an adult, with a maximum of two children under 8 per adult. Single sex and mixed changing rooms with individual cubicles. Crèche available for under 5's Monday-Friday 9.30am-1.30pm. Toddler Splash: Monday, Wednesday and Friday 11am-12noon. Parents and Babies: Tuesday 10.11pm. Aqua Trim: (exercise class suitable for pre and postnatal mums) Monday 8-9pm. AquaNatal: Friday, 10-11am

Springfield Leisure Centre

✉ Beechfield Road, Corsham ☎ 01249 712446
One main 25m pool, chlorinated. Children under 8 years must be accompanied by an adult, with a maximum of two children under 8 per adult. Crèche available Monday 10-11.30am, Tuesday and Wednesday 9.30-11.30am, Thursday 9.15-10.45am, Friday 10am-12noon. Family and Toddlers: Sunday 10-11am. Children's Fun Time: Friday 6-7 pm, Saturday and Sunday 3-4pm

SPORTS CENTRES

Most centres run activities during the school holidays (see Activities and Clubs). Check the local press or phone the centres for details.

Bath Sports and Leisure Centre

✉ North Parade Road, Bath ☎ 462563/5
Open most days 7am-10pm. Facilities include main swimming pool and leisure pool with flume, river ride and water cannons. Badminton and squash courts, a fitness training room, table tennis, a health suite with solarium beds, sauna and plunge pool. Outdoor facilities include a 12/18 hole approach golf course, cricket and football pitches. Various aerobic/keep fit classes, yoga, weights, squash, badminton, bowls available. Adult Recreation: Monday, Wednesday and Friday 9.30am-12.30pm. One ticket allows you to take part in as many activities as you like during the morning. Lift from car park for pushchair and wheelchair access. Crèche available, see *Swimming Pools* above for details.

Castle Place Leisure Centre

✉ Market Street, Trowbridge ☎ 762711
Aerobic and fitness courses, yoga, gym, squash, table tennis etc. Health suite with jacuzzi, sauna, sunbeds, massage and beauty treatments. Crèche available Monday-Friday 9.30am-3.30pm, Saturday 9.30am-12.30pm, Sunday 10.30am-12.30pm. For children from 6 weeks-5 years. Space for 10 children (4 places for under 2's), so you do need to book. You can leave your child for up to 2 hours and you must stay on the premises. Scallywags Tumble Time: Wednesday 1.45-3.45pm Bouncy castle, soft play and ball pond (under 5's). Junior sessions including karate, short tennis, football, after school and Saturday clubs (team games, bouncy castle etc.) and fitness class (for over 5's), also gym class (for 11-16 year olds).

Christie Miller Sports Centre

✉ Lancaster Road, Bowerhill, Melksham ☎ 702826
Various aerobics and fitness classes, badminton, golf bowls, five-a-side, volleyball, squash, netball,

Swimming Pools and Sports Centres

hockey, basketball, cricket, table tennis etc. Crèche available for children up to five years Monday 9.45-11.45am, Tuesday, Thursday and Friday 10am-12noon, Friday 6-6.45pm Ladies Activity Morning: Friday 9.30am-12noon, various sports available. Parent and Toddler Trampolining for under 5's: Thursday 1.30-2pm. Activities for over 5's include: short tennis, trampolining, gymnastics, table tennis, dance, etc.

Clarendon Sports Centre
✉ Frome Road, Trowbridge ☎ 764342
Includes a gym, sports hall, squash courts and swimming pool. No crèche available.

Culverhay Sports Centre
✉ Culverhay School, Rush Hill, Bath
☎ 313104 (9am-4pm) 480882 (after 5pm)
Restricted opening times Monday-Friday 5.30-10pm, Saturday 9.30am-2pm, Sunday 9am-2pm during school terms, 10am-10pm during school holidays. For children aged 8+ Kidsport Saturday 9.30am-12.30pm and Kidstuff 10am-4pm during school holidays. Supervised activities include: trampolining, badminton, cricket, five-a-side, swimming, team games, netball, tennis, hockey, indoor games, competitions. Also various aerobic and fitness sessions, weights room, solarium, and swimming pool. No crèche.

Frome Sports Centre
✉ Princess Anne Road, Frome
☎ 01373 465445
A wide range of exercise classes and sports possible, including archery, badminton, bowls, basketball, hockey, squash, swimming, table tennis, tennis, volleyball, etc. No crèche facilities. Under 3's Playtime: Tuesday 1.30-3.00pm, Wednesday 11am-12.30pm (soft play session). Junior activities include: soft tennis, ballet and tap dancing, gymnastics and trampolining.

Keynsham Leisure Centre
✉ Temple Street, Keynsham ☎ 0117 986 1274
Various activities including swimming, five-a-side football, basket ball, badminton, squash, table tennis, sauna and solarium, fitness room. Crèche available (see **Swimming Pools** for details). Range of activities for under 5's.

The Olympiad Leisure Centre
✉ Monkton Park, Chippenham
☎ 01249 444144
Sports hall, leisure pool, weights and fitness room, squash, health suite with sauna, steamroom, jacuzzi and sunbeds. Crèche:see **Swimming Pools** above. Impressive range of sports and fitness sessions. Under 5's activities include: Toddler Blitz (soft play, trampolines, bouncy castle, ball pool) Tuesday 10am-4pm, Thursday and Saturday 10am-12noon. All children must be accompanied by an adult. Pre-school gymnastics, ballet and tap classes, under 5's trampolining. Junior (up to 16 years) activities include: trampolining, gym, karate, basketball, football, table tennis, squash, volleyball, roller hockey, badminton, five-a-side, netball, cricket, swimming etc.

Springfield Leisure Centre
✉ Beechfield Road, Corsham ☎ 01249 712846
Facilities include sports hall, swimming pool, health suite with sauna, jacuzzi, solarium and steam room, fitness room and squash courts. Crèche available (see **Swimming Pools** for details). Various aerobic and fitness, classes, yoga, squash, badminton, tennis, football, netball, hockey, basketball, volleyball, cricket, bowls etc. Under 5's activities include: Bounce About: Wednesday 9.30 -11.30am. Jumping Juniors: Tuesday 9.30-10.15 am. Over 5's: football, gymnastics, trampolining, swimming, badminton, dance classes.

Trips at a Glance

Adventure Playgrounds
Avon Valley Country Park
Bowood House
Brokerswood
Longleat House
Windmill Hill City Farm

Animals and Birds
Avon Valley Country Park
Bristol Zoo
Chewton Cheese Dairy
Dyrham Park
Lackham
Longleat
Norwood Farm
Pigs Folly
Rode Bird Gardens
Slimbridge Wild Fowl Trust
Windmill Hill City Farm

Ducks to Feed
Canal – Widcombe
Canal – Sydney Gardens
Parade Gardens
Victoria Park

Good for a Rainy Day
All indoor Bath venues
Bristol Industrial Museum
Cheddar Caves
Chewton Cheese Dairy
Corsham Underground Caves
Libraries – books and toys
Markets, Toy shops, Shopping Centres
Soft Play Centres and Swimming Pools
The Exploratory
Wells
Windmill Hill City Farm
Wookey Hole

House and Grounds
Bowood House
Corsham Court
Dyrham Park
Lacock Abbey
Longleat
Sheldon Manor
The American Museum

Nature Trails and Walks
Avon Valley Country Park
Brokerswood
Westonbirt Arboretum
Willsbridge Mill

Train Rides
Avon Valley Railway
Brokerswood
East Somerset Railway
Longleat House (miniature)
Rode Bird Gardens (miniature)

Trips and Jaunts

The Bath area is bursting with places to visit and things to see. These are all child-friendly trips with the ingredients of a good day out for ALL the family. Facilities such as changing rooms, highchairs, children's menus, play and picnic areas are mentioned when present along with buggy accessibility. Unless otherwise stated all venues are well-signposted, have loos, a shop, free parking and a dog ban. If places are easily accessible by public transport, we mention it. We've included prices to give you an idea how much a trip will cost. They were correct at time of writing, but will of course change. We have tried hard to give accurate opening hours and seasonal information, but recommend you telephone to check before visiting as dates may vary from year to year.

PLEASE NOTE When visiting farms, country museums and parks pregnant women should avoid contact with pregnant ewes or newborn lambs due to the risk of infection with chlamydia which causes spontaneous abortion in humans and ewes.

TRIPS AND JAUNTS IN BATH

The American Museum

✉ Claverton Manor, Claverton Down ☎ 460503
Bus 18, get off at The Avenue, 10 minutes walk. Open end March to end October, Tuesday–Sunday 2-5pm, Monday closed except during August and Bank Holidays. Bank Holiday Sunday and Monday 11am–5pm. House and Gardens: Adults £5, over 5s £2.50. Gardens only: Adults £2, over 5s £1.00. Season ticket, membership and family ticket available. Over a dozen furnished period rooms illustrating American life between 17th and 19th centuries. American Indian campfires, buffalo heads, ship's cabin and old Inn kitchen with free home-made gingerbread cooked in the fireside oven. Magnificent quilt collection. Galleries in gardens a bit of a strain with a toddler but lawns and arboretum lovely for a run around. Don't miss railroad car, waggon and tepee. Loos (could change baby in ladies), picnic area, café. Eat inside or on terrace. Buggy outside only. Dogs on a lead.

Bath Abbey Heritage Vaults

✉ South side of Bath Abbey under Kingston pavements ☎ 422462
Monday–Saturday: 10am-4pm. Adults £2 Bath & N E Somerset residents and children free. Restored vaults with Saxon and Norman carvings and presentations of Abbey's 1600 year history. Very interesting for older children but toddlers will get bored. No loos.

Bath Industrial Heritage Centre

✉ Julian Road ☎ 318348
Bus 2. Parking on-street can be difficult. Not well signposted. Open every day Easter-end October 10am-4.30pm. November-Easter weekends only, 10am-4.30pm . Adults £3.50 Qver 5s £2.50 Family £7.50. Mr Bowler's fizzy pop business and light engineering firm closed in 1969. Nothing had been thrown away in 97 years. Anyone aged over three will be fascinated by this reconstruction of offices, bottling rooms and foundry. Good place to go if you're looking for something a bit different. Toddlers will try to touch everything – including working gas lamps. Also a reconstructed stone mine exhibit and cabinet-maker's workshop. Ballance Street park nearby good for letting off steam afterwards (see **Parks and Play Areas**). Loos, café. Lots and lots of steps up and sometimes narrow inside. Not for double buggies.

Bath Postal Museum

✉ 8 Broad Street ☎ 460333
Podium car park. Post Office bus stop. Open all year Monday-Saturday 11am-5pm, Sunday 2-5pm. Adults £2.50 Children £1 Family £6. Bath &

Trips and Jaunts

N E Somerset residents free. The world's first stamp was sent from here on 2nd May 1840. Surprisingly large premises with models and mock-up of Post Office where the first "Penny Black" was issued. Video. Airmail room and temporary exhibitions. Loos. Self-service drinks (leave money in box). Single buggy only.

Beckford's Tower

▣ Lansdown Road, just after the cemetery
☎ 312917
Limited parking. Bus 2 or Park and Ride. Adults £2, under 10's free. April-October weekends and Bank Holiday Monday's 2-5pm. View from the top of 156-step tower is the best bit. Kids love galloping up the spiral staircase. View from behind glass. Small museum at base of tower has model of tower and abbey plus items about Beckford. Nice to combine with walk across the racecourse (see **Walks**). No facilities. No buggies or dogs.

The Building of Bath Museum

▣ The Countess of Huntingdon's Chapel, The Vineyards, The Paragon ☎ 333895
Walcot and Broad Street car parks. Bus 2. Open mid February-mid December Tuesday-Sunday 10.30am-5pm. Open Bank Holidays. Adults £3 Children £1. Discover how Bath's architectural masterpieces were created - how each house was put together from laying foundations to last lick of paint. Lots of models, displays and tools to keep infant-plus ages happy. A Bath Preservation Trust museum housed in a Gothic-style former chapel. Toilets with space to change baby.

Claverton Pumping Station

▣ Ferry Lane, Claverton ☎ 0117 9867536
Off A36, over canal and railway. By canal towpath from Bath. Bus 253, 264. Restricted parking on steep hill. Open Easter to mid October, Sundays and Bank Holidays (except May Day BH) 10.30am-5pm. Machinery running on 4th Sunday in the month, Adults £2 Over 5s £1. Other Sundays, £1.00 and 50p. 19th century water wheel and beam engine. Silent, ``green'' and beautiful to watch. Once pumped water from river to canal, now works for pleasure. Interest to pre-school and above. Friendly, small and quiet. Beware of the trains and fast-running water. Picnic area and counter sales. No buggies or dogs.

Holbourne Museum and Crafts Study Centre

▣ Great Pulteney Street
☎ 466669
Open Monday- Saturday: 11am-5pm, Sunday: 2.30-5.30pm. Closed Mondays. November-Easter. Closed mid December–mid February. Adult £3.50 Children £1.50 Family £7. Membership. Sir Thomas Holbourne's collection of 18th century furniture, paintings, silver and porcelain. Also 20th century artists/craftsmens work. Suitable for well-behaved juniors. Excellent, inexpensive (some free) events for children aged seven-plus held in holidays and half-terms. Past themes include stencilling, marbling and card-making. Loos, sales, garden at rear for picnics. Tea rooms in gardens open 11am-5pm for teas and lunches (see **Eating Out**). Leave buggies in entrance hall. Backpacked babies allowed in galleries.

Museum of Costume and Assembly Rooms

▣ Bennett Street
☎ 477752 /477000
Open Monday- Saturday: 10am-5pm, Sunday: 11am-5pm. Adults £3.50 Over 8s £2.20. Combined ticket with Roman Baths Adults £7 Children £4 Family £17.60. Residents free. Regular free guided tours or free personal audio tour useful for going at your own pace. 400 years of fashion often displayed in period room settings and scenes of Bath. Some look eerie in dim light (to preserve materials). Others, such as the children's party are lovely. Fans, wigs, buckles and gloves will fascinate infants. Otherwise junior age plus. Weddings exhibition until 1998. Displays behind floor-to-ceiling glass. Free access for all to Assembly rooms, four main rooms with spectacular chandeliers, fireplaces and paintings, if not in use. Loos, room to feed and change in Ladies.

Museum of East Asian Art

▣ 12 Bennett Street (opposite Museum of Costume) ☎ 464640
Open April-October, Monday-Saturday: 10am-6pm, Sunday: 10am-5pm. November to March Monday-Saturday: 10am-5pm, Sunday: 12 noon-5pm. Adults £3, Under 12s free. Over 500 treasures, including jades, ceramics, metalwork, bamboo and soapstone carvings, from China, Tibet, Mongolia, Japan, Korea, Thailand and Burma. Museum shop selling crafts and gifts. Not buggyable.

Trips and Jaunts

No 1 Royal Crescent

☎ 428126

On-street parking. Open March-end October, Tuesday-Sunday 10.30am-5pm. Open Bank Holiday and Bath Festival Mondays. Open November-mid December, Tuesday-Sunday 10.30am-4pm. Adult £3.50 Over 5s £2.50 Family £8. Keep ticket for 50p off Building of Bath Museum. Georgian House restored and furnished to original state. Kitchens fun to look at, otherwise valuable exhibits make it a bit of a headache for parents. Junior age plus. Run by Bath Preservation Trust. Loos downstairs. Not buggyable.

Prior Park Landscape Garden

✉ Ralph Allen Drive ☎ 833422

Open 6 days a week, closed Tuesday, 12 noon-5.30pm (or dusk if earlier). Adults £3.80 Children £1.90 National Trust members free. No parking at or near the gardens. Buses 2 or 4 from Grand Parade and Bus Station Monday-Saturday, Sunday and Bank Holidays dedicated service every half hour. 3 parking bays at the garden for disabled, call 833422 in advance to book space. Beautiful and intimate 18th century landscape garden set in sweeping valley with breathtaking views towards the lakes and Bath. Created by Bath entrepreneur Ralph Allen with the help of poet Alexander Pope and Lancelot 'Capability' Brown. Recently restored. Not so good for active toddlers as you have to stick to the path.

Roman Baths Museum

✉ Abbey Church Yard ☎ 477774

Open April-September daily 9am-6pm. October-March Monday-Saturday: 9.30am-5pm, Sunday: 10.30am-5pm. Adults £5.60 Children £3.30 Family £14.30. Combined ticket with Museum of Costume Adult £7.50 Children £4 Family £17.60. Bath residents free. Guided tours are excellent (Signing Guide for the deaf) or use free personal audio tour. See steaming hot mineral water gush out of the ground and bubble up in Roman Baths dating from 1st and 5th centuries. See Roman charms, goddesses, statues, animated computer reconstruction of Baths and Temple, models to see and touch. Rivetting stuff for over 5s, OK for some over 3's. Leave pushchairs behind a screen near entrance. A sturdy backpack (for under 4s) is loaned free. Loos and tiny feeding/changing cupboard near Pump Room and also near shop. Pump Room has highchairs and helpful staff. Pricey (see **Eating Out**). Listen to the Pump Room trio for free and pay to try Bath water.

Royal Photographic Society

✉ Milsom Street

☎ 462841

Open Monday-Sunday 9.30am-5.30pm. Adults £2.50 Children over 7 £1.75. Membership. Annual pass. National Centre of Photography with permanent history of photography museum and other temporary exhibitions in city-centre site which incorporates an octagonal chapel. Junior age kids and above. Children's workshops in school holidays very popular. Book well ahead. Loos, baby-changing in ladies. Ask at museum desk for access to feeding room. Café downstairs (see **Eating Out**). Steps up to museum – carry buggies. Temporary exhibitions on ground floor.

Sally Lunn's Refreshment House and Museum

✉ 4 North Parade Passage

☎ 461634

In a narrow alley off Abbey Green. Ham Gardens car park. Open Monday-Friday 10am-5pm; Saturday 10am-6pm and Sunday 12-6pm. Also Bank Holidays. Restaurant open until 11pm except Monday. Museum charge Adult 30p. Children free. Oldest house in Bath with all-day restaurant on ground floor serving menu largely based on Sally Lunn buns. Small basement museum with 17th century bread oven, pots and pans. Taped recording of information. Remains of Roman, Saxon and Medieval buildings can be seen along with stalactites and stalagmites. Half an hour on a wet day for junior age kids. Loos.

Victoria Art Gallery

✉ Pulteney Bridge

☎ 477772

Open Monday-Friday 10am-5.30pm, Saturday 10am-5pm, closed Sunday and Bank Holidays. Free entry for all. First floor permanent collection of paintings and ground floor large and small galleries for touring exhibitions, local and contemporary artists. You may have to work hard to keep young children's interest. Loos. Buggy possible, but steps up from street and stairs to first floor galleries. Disabled access in Bridge Street with bell.

Bath with your Kids

Trips and Jaunts

William Herschel Museum
✉ New King Street ☎ 311342
Best to park at Charlotte Street car park. Not well signposted. Open March-end October daily 2-5pm. November-end February weekends only 2-5pm. Adults £2.50 Children £1 Family £5 Astronomer and musician William Herschel discovered the planet Uranus with a home-made telescope from this house in 1781. Now a museum, workshop, gardens, kitchen and other period rooms with telescopes, musical mementoes and more. Suitable for Junior age plus. Loo. Counter sales. Leave buggies in hallway.

Open Top Bus Tours

'Live' guided tours for main tourist sites in Bath centre. Badgerline also goes up Widcombe Hill for splendid views of the city. Fun for over 3's if you sit upstairs. Smaller children may get bored! Buggies fine folded downstairs. Main starting point at Terrace Walk (near Abbey). All day Tickets and you can hop off and on as you please.

Badgerline/Guide Friday – Green/cream buses
☎ 444102/464446
Also starts from bus station. Tours last approx.1 hour. Summer 9.30am-5pm every 15 minutes, winter Monday-Friday 10.15am-2.15pm hourly, weekends 9.45am-2.45pm every half hour. Adults £6.50, over 5's £2, Residents £2. Tour goes up Widcombe Hill and down North Road - excellent views. On a fine day you could get off at University and walk to American Museum. Keep your ticket for discounts at various tourist attractions.

City Tours– Red/white buses
☎ 424157
Tour lasts approx.45 minutes. Summer 9.45am-4.30pm every 15 minutes, winter 10am-3pm every half hour. Adults £4.50, over 5's £1.50, family £11. Hold on to your ticket for discounts at various tourist attractions.

Regency Tours – Blue/yellow buses
☎ 891174
45 minute tour, 10am–dusk every half hour. No buses in winter. Adults £3.80 children free, no reduction for Bath residents.

Guided Walks

Mayor of Bath's Guides
Free daily tours of historic city centre starting outside Pump Room in Abbey Church Yard all year round. Sunday 10.30am and 2.30pm, Monday-Friday 10.30am and 2.00pm, Saturday 10.30am. Additional tours May-September Tuesday, Friday and Saturday at 7.00pm.

Ghost Walks
☎ 463618
Start and finish at Garrick's Head pub next to Bath Theatre Royal. 30-40 ghost stories told during evening walk around centre city. 8pm-ish-10pm. May-October, Monday-Friday. November-April, Friday's only. Adults £3 Over 8s and concessions £2. Pre-booked children's tours (suitable for birthdays) starting 6.30pm onwards tailored to suit.

An Appointment with Fear
☎ 01904 700945
A ghostly walk through Bath with costumed guides. Starts outside the Pump Room 8pm, lasts approximately one hour. Adults £3.50 Children £2.50.

Trips Afloat – Boat Hire

Bath Boating Station
✉ Forester Road, Bathwick
☎ 466407
Open daily April-September 10am-6pm. Free entry. Rowing boats, punts £3.50 per person per hour, under 13's half price. Membership entitles you to free, unlimited boating for a year and reduced rates for 3 guests. Infants free. Victorian boating station with wooden skiffs and punts for hire (also punting tuition). Delightful lazy outing. Look out for kingfishers, swans and other wildlife. Café, balcony restaurant and bar with good menu for lunch,teas, dinner. Outside tables. Child friendly. No dogs on boats. Double buggy OK.

Bathford
☎ 859847
Rowing boats, canoes and skiffs. April-October.

Trips and Jaunts

Bath and Dundas Canal Company
✉ Monkton Combe (A36 Viaduct Inn/Kennet and Avon Canal) ☎ 722292
Self-drive electric day boats from boatyard at bottom of Brassknocker Hill near Dundas Aquaduct. Toilets in boatyard. Buggies ok on board, life jackets for kids available.

Bristol Packet
☎ 0117 9268157
Rowing boats for hire off Wapping Wharf to explore the floating harbour from the water. Weekends and daily during school holidays from late May to September. Has life jackets.

TRIPS AFLOAT – BOAT TRIPS

Kennet and Avon Canal Trust
☎ 462313
Return trips on 'Jubilee' (35 passengers) from Bath top lock to Bathampton and Claverton Pump. Every Saturday Easter to end October, 11.30am returning 3pm. May to September also 3.30pm returning at 6pm. Special Bank Holiday Sunday and Monday trips 12 noon returning 5.30pm. Toilets and refreshments on board. Buggies OK.

Pulteney Bridge
☎ 466407
Trips up the river to Bathampton leave on the hour every hour, 50 minute round trip. Refreshments and toilets on the larger boats 'Avon Monarch' and 'Sir William Pulteney'. Buggies OK on all boats. Daily from 11am-5pm, April to end October. Weekends only November, February and March.

Bradford-on-Avon
☎ 864378/01380 721279
Public and charter trips along the canal from the wharf. One hour trip west to Avoncliff Aquaduct. Easter to end September, Sundays 2pm and 4.30pm. July and August also Wednesday and Saturday 2.30pm and Sunday 11am. Folded buggies OK.

Bristol Ferry Boat Company
☎ 0117 9273416
Trips around the city docks calling at ss Great Britain. Every 20 minutes, round trip of about 40 minutes. Daily Easter to end September. Weekends only in winter.

Bristol Packet Company
☎ 0117 9268157
Trips on 1920's river steamer 'Tower Belle' or narrowboat 'Redshank'. Various trips around historic floating harbour, up Avon gorge under the suspension Bridge to the Bristol Channel, a 5 hour one way trip to Bath and trips along the River Avon with stops at pubs and tea gardens. Easter to September. Also private party hire.

ss Waverley and Balmoral
☎ 01446 720656
World's last sea-going paddle steamer and pleasure steamer. Day, afternoon and evening trips from Clevedon and Bristol. Toilets. Open Easter-October.

TRIPS AND JAUNTS OUTSIDE BATH

SEE MAP ON PAGES 140/1

1. Avon Valley Country Park
✉ Pixash Lane, Bath Road, Keynsham
☎ 0117 9864929
Open end March-October, Tuesday-Sunday 10am-6pm, Bank Holidays and Mondays in August. Adults £3.25, over 2s £2.25. Children must be accompanied by an adult. Riverbank setting. Well-marked trail with adventure play equipment, rare cattle, sheep, ducks, goats, wallabies etc. View deer from a hide, row on the pond, hire a fishing rod or play Mini golf. Water is unfenced. Summer events and activity days for children. Basic café and loos, in and outdoor picnic area, riverside barbecues for use free. Excellent free brochure. Double and single buggy access.

2. Avon Valley Railway
✉ Bitton Station, Willsbridge, Bristol
☎ 0117 9327296 talking timetable
☎ 0117 9325538 weekend enquiries
Site, buffet and shop open every weekend, all year. Steam trains operate at weekends - check timetable for dates. Roughly every Sunday in July and August otherwise first Sunday of month plus four days at Easter. Free site admission, charge for trains: Adults £3 over 5s £1. Family ticket. Membership. Enthusiast-run steam

Bath with your Kids 117

Trips and Jaunts

railway and yard. Old rolling stock and yard worth a quick visit, longer if trains are running (Bitton Station to Oldland Common). Walks to Willsbridge Mill and on Avon Valley path. Santa Specials and other events during year. Loos, stand-up chips and chilled drinks in old station buffet or eat in old restaurant car. Picnic area. Single buggy access. Dogs allowed on leads.

3. Bowood House

✉ Calne/Chippenham ☎ 01249 812102

Daily April-start November 11am-6pm (or dusk). Garden centre open all year and garden for 6 weeks May-June. Adult £4.80 over 5s £2.60. Season ticket. No dogs. Once your children are in Bowood's spectacular adventure playground it is unlikely they will want to come out to look round the Georgian house, gardens, hermit's cave and waterfall, never mind the garden centre and parkland. Adventure playground for under 13s only. Best enjoyed by ages six to ten. Not very suitable for toddlers - although there are things for them. Looks frighteningly large to adults, children love it. Loos, baby changing, café has highchairs and kids portions. Restaurant and picnic area. Double buggy OK.

4. Brokerswood and Woodland Heritage Museum

✉ Near Westbury, Wiltshire (off the A36 south of Bath) ☎ 01373 822238

Summer: 10am-6pm but can stay in parkland until dusk. Winter: 10am-5pm but museum only open weekends. Railway runs 12 noon-4pm in autumn and closes after October half term until Easter, except for pre-booked Santa Specials at Christmas. Adults £2.50 Accompanied under 14s free (up to 4 kids per family). Season ticket. Soft play room free during week, 50p/half hour weekends. Always very enthusiastically reviewed! A lovely inexpensive day out in an unspoilt 80 acre broad-leaved wood with paths to wander and trees to clamber. Ducks and geese keen to be fed. Extra 50p charge for 10 minute train ride through forest. Adventure playground for 3-12 year olds. Attractive museum with lots of "hands-on" displays, good for 7+. Special events throughout year. All facilities are shared with the camping site. Loos, baby changing room (accessible to men and women). Play and picnic areas. Very good café, will do children's portions on request, very friendly and nothing is too much trouble. Shop sells pocket-money priced things. Most of the main woodland paths are buggyable, but it's hard work. Dogs allowed.

5. Cheddar Showcaves and Cheddar Gorge

✉ Cheddar Gorge, Somerset ☎ 01934 742343

Free parking up gorge on cave side. Other parking £1-3.50. Summer park and ride from Broadway Caravan Park. Open daily Easter-September 10am-5pm, October-Easter 10am-4.30pm. Adult £6.50 Children 5-15 £3.95. Family ticket. Membership. Go on a wet winter morning, take torches and wellies for children to play cavers and you will have a whale of a time without crowds. Can be very busy at other times. Two tours, museum and vertical hike up Jacob's Ladder to observation tower included in ticket. 3 mile gorge walk starts at top of Jacob's Ladder. Allow 2 hours, wear stout footwear and suitable clothing. Gough's Cave has stalagmites and stalactites; Cheddar man and glittering formations (30 minutes). Cox's Cave is narrow (a squeeze with a backpack) with reflecting pools. Possible to leave at Ladye Chapel to avoid Crystal Quest - a frightening fantasy grotto with strobe lights, roaring dragons etc. Adventure caving for over 12s, a one-and-a-half hour exploration of 1000 feet of caves. Can be pre-booked. Loos. Baby-changing OK for fathers (feeding here too). Indoor play and picnic area (play cave). Café with highchair open as caves. Double buggies OK in Gough's Cave only - apart from one circular loop.

6. Chewton Cheese Dairy

✉ Chewton Mendip ☎ 01761 241666

Not well signposted, but easy journey. Open every day except Thursday and Sunday 10am-4.30pm. Best time to see things 12-2.30pm. Restaurant open daily 10am-4.30pm. Free unless you take tour which includes video. September 11.30, 12.15 and 1.00pm. Adults £2.50, Children £1.50, Family £6. Includes visit to farm animals and owls plus free cheese samples. Animals can be seen without tour and cheese-making viewed from restaurant balcony. Loos, café in old priory garden with in and outdoor seating. Picnics. Pine-clad restaurant overlooking dairy with highchairs and children's books. Hot and cold food, yummy cakes and puddings with mountains of cream from the dairy. Double buggy OK - carry it up to cheese-making viewing gallery.

118 Bath with your Kids

Trips and Jaunts

7. Corsham Court
☎ 01249 712214
Open 1st January-30th November, 2-4.30pm. Closed Monday and Friday. From Good Friday-30th September, open Fridays and Bank Holidays to 6pm. House and Garden Adults £4.50 Children £2.50, less for gardens only. Peacocks, Gothic bath house and Elizabethan architecture to admire from outside. Walks along gravel paths around lake and grounds by Capability Brown and Repton. Discreet picnics possible. Inside - best suited for over fives - an excellent collection of Italian and Flemish paintings. Single buggy only. Loos in house.

8. Corsham Underground Quarry
✉ Park Lane, Corsham ☎ 01249 716288
Open Easter Sunday and Monday, April Sundays only, May to September daily except Fridays, October Sundays only. Hour-long underground tours start at 10.15am (not Saturday), 11.45am, 2pm and 3.30pm. Adults £3.60, Over 5s £2.20. The 159 steps up and down should not put you off going with a buggy or backpack as the underground route is very flat and wide. Fascinating for pre-school and above. Everyone wears a hard hat, carries a battery pack and light for this guided tour of the Bath stone mining process. Machinery, graffiti, carvings and excellent guide. Not at all claustrophobic. Take warm clothes - the temperature is fairly stable underground. Loos and picnic area. Single buggies only.

9. Dyrham Park
✉ On A46, M4 junction 18 ☎ 0117 937 2501
House open April-end October daily except Wednesday and Thursday 12noon-5.00pm (or dusk if earlier). Park open daily 12noon-dusk. House, gardens and park: Adults £5.50, Park only: Adults £1.60, children aged 5-17 half price. National Trust members free. Huge deer park to explore and picnic in. Deer and cows roam free. Wonderful views across to Wales. Can be fairly muddy and too rough for buggies - backpacks only. Impressive plants in orangery. Formal gardens at rear with steep-sided lake. House not for itchy-footed toddlers. Loos, café with highchairs serves teas, ice cream etc. Buggies OK in Stables Restaurant, terrace garden and ground floor of house. Double buggies OK too. Dogs in dog walking area only.

10. East Somerset Railway
✉ Cranmore Railway Station (A361 Shepton Mallet-Frome road) ☎ 01749 880417
Opening times - definitely best to phone and check! Basically 10am-4pm, every day during July and August, varying open days for other months of the year. December: weekends on pre-booked Santa Specials. Train ride and viewing: Adults £4.75, children 3-16 £3. Viewing only: Adults £2, Children 3-16: £1. Train rides not too long and can be repeated as many times as you like during the day. Engine shed, station, workshops, signal box and museum to explore on steaming and non-steaming days. Beautifully renovated engine. Good picnic sites next to railway and play area with swings and climbing frames. Buffet car restaurant has yummy cakes and homemade food for lunch, tea or snacking. Children's portions available. Dogs on leads.

11. Farleigh Hungerford Castle
✉ Farleigh Hungerford (signposted off A36 after Limpley Stoke) ☎ 754026
Open summer daily 10am-6pm, winter Wednesday-Sunday 10am-4pm. Adults £2 over 5's £1. 45 minute audio tour included. English Heritage members free. Charges increase drastically for special events. Ruined 14th century castle with small exhibition, chapel with spooky crypt and grounds with lovely views. Ideal for peaceful afternoon picnics. Lots of places to scamper around. Some steep drops. Medieval tournament days are fun. Clean loos, picnics encouraged, but no benches. Catering provided on events days. Double buggy possible for much of it. Dogs on leads.

12. Iford Manor Gardens
✉ Westwood, near Bradford-on-Avon ☎ 863146
Open May-September: 2-5pm daily except Monday and Friday. April and October: 2-5pm Sundays and Easter. Adults £2.20 Under 10s free. Stunning terraced gardens with lots of pools, statues, colonnades, cloisters and beautiful flower beds. Lots of space for children to run around but be careful of toddlers and ponds. Best to backpack it! Teas available weekends and bank holidays May-August. Toilets clean. Plenty of parking and a good picnic spot outside gardens, across medieval bridge, follow footpath on right for 200 yards and access to river. Some lovely woodland walks in the area as well. Can be combined with stop at the Inn at Freshford just down the road (See **Pubs**).

Bath with your Kids

Trips and Jaunts

13. Lackham Gardens and Museum

✉ Off A350 between Lacock and Chippenham
☎ 01249 443111

Open April-October 11am-5pm. Last admission 4pm Adults £3 Over 5s £1. Family ticket and season ticket. A good-value day out with no extra costs. Rare breed animals; old farm buildings museum stuffed with agricultural machinery and equipment. Walled gardens and greenhouses with 33 displays. Plants and produce for sale. Riverside/woodland trail. Picnic area and ageing play/adventure area with an old tractor. Basic loos, can't get a buggy in. Café overlooking gardens is incredibly cheap with nice cakes. Double buggies OK - woodland walks might be dodgy on wet days. Dogs on lead.

14. Lacock Village

✉ A350 south of Chippenham ☎ 01249 730227 (Abbey) ☎ 730459 (museum)

Museum: open March-October, daily 11am-5.30pm. November-February, weekends only 11am-4pm. Adults £2.30 over 5's £1.10. Abbey: open April-October, daily (except Tuesday), 1-5.30pm. Cloisters and Grounds: open April-October, daily 12-5.30pm. Cloisters and Grounds only Adults £2.10 over 5's £1.00. House and Grounds Adults £4.20 over 5's £2.20. National Trust Members Free.

A Sunday afternoon strolling place. National Trust village dating back to Middle Ages with good-food pubs & teashops, craft shops and Tithe barn for browsers. Abbey with cloisters, brewery buildings and unusual trees in grounds. Museum of photography near Abbey entrance. Picnics in playing field and by river only. Loos by car park and Abbey. No dogs. No buggies in house or museum. Play area near car park. Good pubs and teas in village.

15. Longleat House and Gardens

✉ Off A36 Warminster bypass ☎ 01985 844400

House open daily except Christmas Day. Easter-September 10am-6pm. Phone for other opening times. Other attractions open daily from mid March-end October 10/11am-5.30pm. Grounds only Adult £2 Children 50p. Pay as you go for individual attractions or buy Passport Ticket for grounds, house and all attractions including Safari Park Adult £12 Children £10. Unused parts of ticket can be used for up to a year. Don't try and do it all in a day. It is worth pacing yourself. Can be expensive if only a few individual attractions are visited. Children will love the adventure playground-cum-castle, boat and train rides most. Pay once for adventure playground and you can be re-admitted same day free. Pets Corner (looks sad), huge maze, dolls houses, Victorian houses, models, old vehicles, butterflies, bygones, Dr Who exhibit and of course the house will appeal according to age. Don't underestimate the interest in formal fountains and fish ponds! Loos of various quality in restaurant, cafe and stable block. Pub has a baby changing room available to fathers too. Could change in old stable block loos. Play area and picnic area near car park. Good picnicking near lake. Assorted food outlets including pub and cellar cafe (both with highchairs and small portions). Cafe reasonably priced. Fast-food available near car park. Opening hours and seasons for catering outlets vary, telephone 01985 844893 (cafe) 01985 844253 (restaurant/pub). Easy buggying. Dogs on lead. No dogs in Maze, Adventure Castle, butterfly garden and animal reserves.

RARE BEASTS!

Visit **NORWOOD** for a fascinating look at farming at its ecological best. *Just 15 minutes from the centre of Bath*-Many **rare and beautiful breeds** of sheep, cattle, pigs, goats, ponies and poultry. A **delightful spot** to bring the whole family for a picnic, a country walk and a taste of our delicious home-made refreshments. We are a **recycling centre** too, so remember to load up the car with your bottles, papers, old clothing and cans! A **modern Windturbine** provides enough power for the needs of the refrigerators and lighting in the farm shop, with even a little left over on windy days for hot water!

FARM SHOP SELLING OUR OWN ORGANIC MEAT and vegetables in season

Open every day between March 22nd and September 21st 10.30am - 6pm

Admission: Adults £3.50, Students & OAPs £3, Children £2.

School parties by arrangement, Reductions for parties, Birthday parties catered for. Season tickets available, Pushchair and wheelchair accessible. Sorry - only guide dogs allowed

Norwood Farm, Bath Rd, Norton St Philip, Somerset. Tel: 01373 834356

On the B3110 half way between Bath & Frome, Trowbridge and Radstock

Trips and Jaunts

16. Longleat Safari Park
✉ Off A36 Warminster bypass ☎ 01985 844328
Train to Warminster, Frome, Westbury. Badgerline bus connects to main gate. Open March-November 10am-6pm (or sunset). Adults £5.50 Over 4s £4 See house and garden section for details of discount ticket. The most relaxing way to see these free-range animals is by safari bus from outside Pets Corner:Adults £2, children £1. It saves having your windscreen wipers stripped by the monkeys and worrying whether a rhino is about to charge you. Plus the car driver actually gets to see something. Driver's commentary is excellent and the bus stops en-route. For self-drivers, park is zoned, patrolled and reassuringly well-staffed. Can get out in designated picnic/cafe/stopping area. Free dog kennelling provided at entrance to safari park.

17. Norwood Farm
✉ Norton St Philip on B3110
☎ 01373 834356
Bus X3 from Bath bus station, then 10-15 minute walk up lane (buggyable). Open daily Easter-end September 10.30am-6pm. Adult £3 Over 3s £2. Season ticket Adult £9 Over 3s £6. Excellent for most ages - 9 months up to 10 years. Schools and playgroups welcome, worksheets available. Pregnant women will want to avoid contact with ewes during lambing season - just don't feed them! Shop open all year, ring for details, sells animal-related goods, some at pocket money prices, also organic meat, vegetables and milk. Clean and happy atmosphere where visitors can buy food to feed animals as they walk round pens, fields and coops. Pig-feeding time (4.15pm daily) is a highlight. High site can be windy, so wrap up well. In dry weather reasonable for a double buggy. Loos with table suitable for changing babies on. Play area with two tractors and large felled trees for climbing on. Very clean café with highchairs. Picnic area. Home-produced food and wonderful cakes.

18. Pigs Folly
✉ Cold Ashton, near Marshfield (on A420, 200 yards from A46 roundabout)
☎ 891849/859576
Open all year round, just walk in on a donation basis (box by gate), suggest £1. Lovely farm, very friendly towards children. Animals outside around large enclosure with ride-on toys for children. Baby animals if its the right time of year. Organic meat, eggs etc on sale.

19. Priston Mill
✉ Priston
☎ 423894/429894
Only accessible by own transport. Best to telephone for seasonal opening hours, but basically Easter-end September: Tuesday-Friday during school holidays 2.15-5pm, weekends and Bank Holidays 11am-5.30pm. Adults £2.50, Children £1.75. Season ticket £12.75 for up to 2 adults and 3 children for 3 visits during the season. Working mill (demonstrations at weekends). Walk 'under' water wheel and up ladder-like stairs. Must carry baby/nervous toddler around mill. Supervise closely. Short nature trail. Watch milking, geese and ducks. Often a trailer ride around farm. Loos, baby changing, play and picnic area. Licensed. restaurant, serves teas and lunches. Buggy some of the way.

20. Radstock, Midsomer Norton and District Museum
✉ Barton Meade House, Haydon, Radstock
☎ 01761 471204 during opening hours
On Radstock-Kilmerston road - Not well-signposted. Saturdays 10am-4pm. Sundays and Bank Holidays 2-5pm. Adults £1.50 Children £1. Over eights would love the reconstructed mining tunnel, miners room, old shop and schoolroom. Piles of exhibits - much on the area's mining history. A toddler could cause havoc here as very little is in display cabinets. Café (Easter-October), loos and picnic area. Not buggy-friendly.

21. Rode Tropical Bird Gardens
✉ Just off A36 at Woolverton ☎ 01373 830326
Bus X3. Open daily except Christmas Day. Summer 10am-6pm, Winter 10am-dusk. Adults £4.30, Children 5-16 £2.30, Family £12.80. Season ticket. Hundreds of colourful, noisy birds in garden setting. Play area is safe but not special. Pets corner uninspiring, but kids enjoy it. Gardens with nice borders. Miniature steam railway through woods runs Easter-September (adult £1, child 80p). Double buggy possible, but some steps. Loos, changing and feeding room OK for fathers. Play and picnic areas, bar

Bath with your Kids 121

Trips and Jaunts

and café for teas and lunches in summer. Winter light refreshments only. Several special events weekends in summer.

22. Sheldon Manor
☏ Chippenham, Wiltshire (mile and a half west of town, signposted from A420) ☎ 01249 653120
Open Easter-start October Sunday, Thursday and Bank Holidays. Garden 12.30-6pm. House 2-6pm. Adults £3.25, Over 11s £1. Interesting family heirlooms and collections. Family atmosphere - and friendly. Indoor and outdoor quiz for kids. Big dolls' house. Large terraced garden, with buggyable paths but steps hard to negotiate, animals, clambering log and lawns. Beware deep pond and swimming pool. Delicious lunches and good-value teas with tables inside or out. Toilets. Mothers' room on request. House unsuitable for buggies. Dogs on lead in gardens only. Picnics fine below road.

23. Slimbridge Wildfowl and Wetlands Centre
☏ Slimbridge, Cam Bridge, Gloucestershire (Junctions 13 and 14 on M5) ☎ 01453 890065
Open daily 9.30am-5pm (4pm in winter). Closed 24-25 December. Adult £4.70 Over 4s £2.35 Family £11.75. Members free. Collection of native, wild and migrating birds in natural wetland habitat. You can't get closer to birds than here - children love the hour-long marked walk through enclosures which can take up to four hours if you feed everything that quacks at you. Take your own bread or buy feed. Excellent indoor activity area, hides and safe observation points. In and outdoor picnic areas, restaurant with highchairs and children's portions. Easily double buggied. Clean loos, baby changing and feeding room accessible to fathers. Relaxed, family friendly day out for all ages. Wrap up well in winter.

24. Stourhead House and Garden
☏ North Stourton, Wiltshire (10 miles south of Frome) ☎ 01747 841152
House open April-October daily except Thursday and Friday 12noon-5.30pm (or dusk). Garden open all year 9am-7pm (or dusk) except for Fete Champetre each July. House or gardens only Adults £4.20, Over 5s £2.20. House and gardens Adults £7.50, Over 5s £3.50. Family ticket (2 adults/2 children) house or gardens £10, house and gardens £20. National Trust members free. The perfect place to wear your toddler out in majestic surroundings. Two main walks - one just over a mile around landscaped lake and exotic garden buildings, the other starting at the top running down through the trees to join lakeside route. Excellent in all seasons. Backpacks only in 18th century house. Buggy OK in gardens but a bit of a push on chippings. Courtyard Café is good, eat indoors or out. Also pub or more pricey restaurant meals in the Spread Eagle next door. Picnic tables near courtyard parking. Picnicking allowed in gardens. National Trust shop open all year. Car park visitor centre with loos and baby changing.

25. Stourhead Alfred's Tower
☎ 01747 841152
As you approach Stourhead from Frome, the tower is well signposted to your right. Open April-October daily except Friday and Monday. Tuesday-Thursday 2-5.30pm. Saturday-Sunday 11.30am-5.30pm (or dusk). Adults £1.50 Children 70p. National Trust members free. A challenge few children can resist - 160' of red brick tower perched on edge of the hill, just waiting to be climbed. Breathtaking views. 221 steps to count. Can be very windy at the top. Need to hang on tight to toddlers as the tower has no roof in the middle. Backpacks only! Nearest facilities Stourhead house and gardens.

26. Wells Cathedral and Close
☎ Cathedral 01749 674483 ☎ Bishop's Palace 01749 678691 ☎ Tourist Office 01749 672552
40 minutes drive from Bath or bus 173 (hourly). Pay for parking. Donation suggested in cathedral Adults £3 Children £1. Bishop's Palace open Easter Saturday-end October Tuesday-Thursday and Bank Holiday Monday, daily in August 10am-6pm, Sundays 2-6pm. Adults £2.50 under 12s free. Cathedral has one of the oldest mechanical clocks in world - knights on horseback joust every quarter and a figure strikes a bell on the hour. Walk via cloisters or market place arch to Bishop's Palace. Moat with hungry ducks and swans that ring a gatehouse bell for food. Walk round moat and find park and play area on right next to Tithe barn and bandstand. Vicars' Close on your right through arch has wonderful chimneys. See Bishop's Palace chapel, Henderson Rooms, grounds and wells. Double buggy OK. Loos and baby room OK for fathers off cloister gardens near Bishop's Palace. Café, in

cloisters, for lunches, teas with good cakes. Open Monday-Saturday 10am-5pm (4.30pm in winter) Sunday 2-5pm. Closed 2 weeks Christmas.

27. Westbury White Horse

Well-signposted from Westbury. No charge. Free car park at top of hill, scramble down slope to white horse. Lovely views from this English Heritage white horse carved in the turf above Bratton. Take a picnic, kite and mud-wrestling gear if wet. Best for babies in backpacks or infant-plus ages. Not really a place to toddle and if you must, take reins. No facilities, but there's often an ice-cream van. Dogs allowed.

28. Westonbirt Arboretum

✉ Westonbirt, Tetbury, Gloucestershire
☎ 01666 880220

Open daily 10am-8pm (or dusk). Adult £2.80, Over 5s £1. Family ticket. Season ticket. Hide-and-seekers paradise. Well-marked walks around 600 acre tree collection. Some along gravel paths, others on rough grass (less well marked). Best for autumn colours and rhododendron's around May-time. Good central information area with facilities. Trees well labelled. Needs several trips to do all the walks. Loos (not suitable for changing but can get a pushchair in.) Café with outdoor seating under shelter only. Picnic area near car park. Double buggy possible. Dogs allowed. Fireworks in November and Father Christmas visits during December, (phone to confirm).

29. Whitehall Garden Centre

✉ Corsham Road, Lacock (right, just before Lacock bypass as you approach from Bath)
☎ 01249 730204

No entrance fee. Poorly signposted. Birds, chipmunks and fish provide the toddler entertainment while adults browse. Small play area with free bouncy castle. Annual Easter bunny hunt. Father Christmas from end of November. Loos. Superb café with plenty of highchairs and space. Very good, reasonably-priced food. Will supply beakers. Double buggy possible. Dogs allowed.

30. Willsbridge Mill Wildlife Trust

✉ Willsbridge Hill, Longwell Green, Bristol (A431/A4175 junction) ☎ 0117 932 6885

On Avon Walkway. Bus 332. Free entry. Open end March-November noon-5pm. Closed Saturday and Monday except Bank Holidays. Mid February-mid March open Sundays only 2-4pm. Imaginative, hands-on exhibition area for 3+. Signposted half-hour jigsaw trail through nature reserve plus another signed walk. 22 acre nature reserve and mill. Stream, ponds, quarry and woods. Activity days detailed in leaflet. Loos. Picnic area, café. Car park a ten-minute stroll from Mill along footpath. Dogs preferred on lead. Pooper-scooper area.

31. Wookey Hole Caves

✉ Wookey Hole, Somerset (2 miles from Wells. M5 junction 22) ☎ 01749 672243

Open daily. Summer 9.30am-5.30pm. Winter 10.30am-4.30pm. Closed 17-25 December. Adults £6 Over 4s £3.50. Family tickets available. Best for children over 4. Guided route through caves, tunnel, valley and mill with paper-making. Fairground museum with barrel organ music, mirror maze, Edwardian penny arcade and more. Cave tour slippery, steep and low in parts, darkness and loudly slammed doors may terrify small children. Buggies impossible in caves, backpack throughout. Loos, baby changing room, cafe with highchairs and children's portions.

BRISTOL

Easily reached by car, bus or train. Bus X3 from Bath Bus Station, or use The Park & Ride from Brislington. Trains run frequently to Bristol Temple Meads, then buses 8, 9, 508 and 509 provide quick link to City Centre, West End, Clifton and Broadmead. Don't forget annual events such as the Balloon Fiesta (August), Kite Festival (September) and Harbour Regatta (August). Further information from the Titch-Hiker's Guide to Bristol (whom we thank for these recommendations) or:

Bristol Tourist Information Office

✉ St.Nicholas Church, St. Nicholas Street
☎ 0117 926 0767

Blaise Castle Museum and Grounds

✉ Henbury Road, Henbury, Bristol BS10 7QS
☎ 0117 950 6789

Open Tuesday-Sunday 10am-1pm, 2-5pm.

Trips and Jaunts

Entrance free. Car parking on Kings Weston Road. 18th Century house with museum of everyday life from 1750-present. Interesting collection of children's toys. Good play area outside, lots of space, woods for long walks.

Bristol Docks

Great fun to wander around the renovated warehouses of Narrow Quay now housing arts centres, cafes, bars etc. Just across the swing bridge in Prince's Wharf is The Industrial Museum. Another 20 minute dawdle down the dockside, past the old pirate ships, takes you to the Maritime Heritage Centre and ss Great Britain.

Bristol Zoo

✉ Clifton ☎ 0117 973 8951
Buses 8, 9, 508 and 509 from Temple Meads. Open daily 9am- 4.30pm in Winter, 5.30pm in Summer. Closed Christmas Day. Summer prices, Adult £6.50 Over 3's £3.50. Annual subscription. Toddlers' Week in July has free entry for under fives, entertainment: Punch & Judy, face-painting, bouncy inflatable etc. Other events during year. Always a success in summer or winter. Well-kept and well-labelled animals, birds and gardens. Feeding times a highlight, so get there early - penguins 12.30pm; sea lions 11.30am and 3.30pm, lions, tigers and leopards 3pm. Reptile house and aquarium popular with tinies. Small pets area for children to stroke animals. Lake with boat rides. Possible queueing at peak holiday times. Loos, baby changing and feeding rooms, play area. Picnicking in gardens OK. Ice cream kiosks. Café and restaurant have highchairs and children's portions. Lots of undercover outdoor seating. OK for double buggy. No dogs.

City Museum and Art Gallery

✉ Queen's Road, Clifton ☎ 0117 922 3571
Adults £2, Under 16's free. Open daily 10am-5pm. Old fashioned museum - stuffed animals and model trains are particularly appealing to under 5's, as is the pilot in the bi-plane suspended from the ceiling! Attractive Egyptology collection. Steps at main entrance - but child friendly once inside. Feeding and changing facilities. Café and shop on ground floor.

Clifton Suspension Bridge and Observatory

☎ 0117 974 1242
Toilets on Clifton side. Play area behind. Observatory usually open 11am-5pm ish, but phone to check. Small fee to Observatory and 'Giant's Cave', an opening to cliff face with views. Tunnel leading to it is steep and narrow, leave pushchairs at entrance. Refreshments. Bridge is illuminated at night.

Exploratory Hands-on Science Centre

✉ Bristol Old Station, Temple Meads
☎ 0117 907 9000 ☎ 0117 907 5000 recorded info.
Web site: http://www.exploratory.org.uk
Train on doorstep. Bus X3. Not well signposted. Free weekend parking in Templegate, weekday partial refund. Forecourt parking is very expensive. Open 10 am - 5pm every day except Christmas week. Adults £5, Over 5's £3.50, Family £15. Tickets last all-day. Under 12s must be accompanied. Season ticket. Why wasn't it like this at school? Understandable, hands-on science for (say) seven-to-ten-year-olds and parents. Even a baby in a backpack will love the light exhibits while anyone over three will get stuck in - particularly on the top floor. Ideal place to spend the day without boring anyone. Exhibitions change regularly. Loos, baby-changing in disabled loos. Shop sells books about science plus home experiments, toys etc at pocket-money prices. Café with highchair. Indoor picnic area near loos. Carry buggy up steps to entrance and between all three floors. Double buggy OK.

Industrial Museum

✉ Prince's Wharf, Wapping Road ☎ 0117 925 1470
Just over swing bridge from the Arnolfini. Open 10am-5pm, Tuesday-Sunday and Bank Holidays. Adults £1, under 16's free. Parking Pay and Display. A real helicopter and Concorde's flight deck are highlights of this transport-dominated museum. See, climb on and touch vehicles powered by horse, steam, petrol – everything from a bicycle to a bus. Also the story of Bristol shipping and a working model railway. Ideal for 3 years+. Loos, counter sales, no café. Buggy easy on ground floor, carry up stairs OK. No dogs. Mayflower Steam Tug, Bristol Harbour Railway and Fairbairn Steam Crane operate outside at certain times of the year.

Trips and Jaunts

ss Great Britain
✉ Great Western Dock, Gas Ferry Road
☎ 0117 926 0680
Bus 511 from Temple Meads. Parking partially refunded at Maritime Heritage Centre where you buy your tickets. Adults £3.90, over 5's £2.70. Designed by Brunel, it represents a vital stage in the transition from sail to steam. Built in Bristol in 1843. Fine for the over 3's. Pushchairs not allowed on board. Vigilance required with intrepid toddlers as there are lots of steps and precipitous drops. Loos. Refreshments. Shop. Video. Ferry service weekends and all Summer. Maritime Heritage Centre (free) tells history of shipbuilding in Bristol, with mock-ups and a working steam dredger.

Windmill Hill City Farm
✉ Philip Street, Bedminster ☎ 0117 963 3252
Open 9am-dusk, Tuesday-Sunday. Donation requested. Membership. City farm with variety of animals you can get very close to. Huge sandpit with lots of toys. Rumpus room (soft play area) opens at various times. Bookings for private parties. Holiday drop-in playscheme, outings and toddler group. Adventure playground for all ages. Loos, infant-size loos and potties near playroom. Picnic area. Café with highchairs and wide variety of cheap food. Watch the animals as you eat. Double buggy fine. No dogs.

FURTHER AFIELD

UNDER 30 MILES FROM BATH

Atwell-Wilson Motor Museum
✉ Downside, Stockley Lane, Calne ☎ 01249 813119
Small collection of vintage and classic cars.

Berkeley Castle
✉ M5 Exit 14/ Gloucester ☎ 01453 810332
Castle, gardens and butterflies.

Chepstow Castle
M4 Welsh side of Severn Bridge.

Cotswold Water Park
✉ Near Cirencester ☎ 01285 861459
80 lakes! Lakes 31, 32 and 34 are best for kids. Ducks, walks, paddling, beaches, play equipment, changing facilities, loos, but no café. Parking charge only.

Devizes Locks
☎ Wiltshire Tourist Info. 01380 729408
29 locks in two miles rise 237' to town.

Fleet Air Museum
✉ Yeovilton ☎ 01935 840565
Hands-on aircraft collection. Adjacent airbase.

Glastonbury
☎ Abbey 01458 832267
Abbey, Tor, Rural Life Museum (see below).

Haynes Motor Museum
✉ Sparkford, Yeovil ☎ 01963 440804
Over 250 cars from around the world.

International Helicopter Museum
✉ Weston-Super-Mare ☎ 01934 635227
World's largest helicopter and auto-gyro collection.

Sea-Life Centre
✉ Weston-super-Mare ☎ 01934 641603
Walk through underwater tunnel. Touch pools. Restaurant and gift shop.

Somerset Rural Life Museum
✉ Glastonbury ☎ 01458 831197
Museum in Tithe Barn. Huge programme of craft demonstrations and farming activities.

Weston-super-Mare Tropicana
☎ 01934 626581
Leisure complex, heated pool etc.

Wye Valley and Tintern Abbey
☎ Tourist Info. 01291 623772 (summer only)

OVER 30 MILES FROM BATH

Avebury
7 miles west of Marlborough. Stone circles, National Trust manor and two other museums. 'Stones' café recommended.

Badger and Wildlife Rescue Centre
✉ Secret World, New Road, East Huntspill
☎ 01278 783250

Bath with your Kids

Trips and Jaunts

Beaulieu House and Motor Museum
✉ Near Southampton ☎ 01590 612345
National Motor Museum. Over 250 vehicles, rides, house and grounds. Wonderful roses in season.

Bourton-on-the-Water Model Village
☎ 01451 820467

Cotswold Wildlife Park
✉ Burford, Oxon ☎ 01993 823006

Cricket St. Thomas Wildlife and Leisure Park
✉ Chard ☎ 01460 30755
Acres of park land. Rides, fun parks and adventure play. TV Leisure park. "Kids love this place! - definitely worth the trip."

Crofton Beam Engines
✉ 6 miles SE Marlborough ☎ 01672 870300
Oldest working beam engines in world.

Didcot Railway Centre
☎ 01235 817200
GWR locos and museum.

Dean Heritage Centre
✉ Forest of Dean ☎ 01594 822170
Mining Museum, miners cottage, adventure playground. Lovely walks in forest all round.

Forest of Dean Sculpture Trail
Starts Beechenhurst Lodge on the B4226

Great Dorset Steam Fair
☎ 01258 860361
Week-long August gathering (starts 1st Wednesday after BH Monday) of steam, traction and other engines. Fairs and crafts.

Great Western Railway Museum
✉ Swindon
☎ 01793 4931189
Five railway locomotives and memorabilia.

Hinckley Power Station
✉ Near Bridgwater
☎ 01278 654334
Nuclear power station visitor centre.

Mary Rose
✉ Portsmouth ☎ 01705 812931
Two minutes walk from Harbour Station (direct train from Bath).

Museum of Advertising and Packaging
✉ Gloucester Docks
☎ 01452 302309

National Bird of Prey Centre
✉ Newent, Herefordshire
☎ 01531 820286

National Waterways Museums
✉ Gloucester Docks
☎ 01452 318054
Canal history. Lots of hands-on children's activities.

Salisbury
☎ Tourist Information 01722 334956
Direct train from Bath or A36 easy drive. The Medieval cathedral has tallest spire in England. Museums etc, market, river, walks.

West Somerset Railway
✉ Minehead, near Taunton ☎ 01643 704996
20 mile ride, steam and diesel trains.

OTHER SOURCES OF INFORMATION

Bath Tourist Information Office
✉ Abbey Chambers, Abbey Churchyard
☎ 477101

Bath Chronicle
✉ 33 Westgate Street ☎ 444044

Venue
☎ 0117 942 8491
Fortnightly listings magazine.

This Month in Bath
☎ 460904
Free monthly 'What's On' listings plus basic tourist information.

The Bath Month
☎ 314322
Another free 'What's On' listing with tourist information and map.

Bath Central Library
✉ The Podium, Northgate Street ☎ 428144
For leaflets and basic tourist information. Upstairs accessible by escalator or lift.

Walks

We have covered a variety of walks both urban and rural in and around Bath - see maps for the start of most of the walks. Most fall within the OS Map Pathfinder No 1183, except for those marked with an asterisk. A grid reference has been given for the start of most walks. To read a map reference, remember "along the corridor and up the stairs". Note that a grid reference applies to road atlases as well as all OS maps. The walks are timed by an adult pushing a pushchair or carrying a back pack. Walks 1 - 13 are those suitable for back packs only. Walks 16 - 22 are possible with a buggy.

Country Code

Happy walking and do remember to observe the country code:
- Guard against all risk of fire
- Fasten all gates
- Keep dogs under proper control
- Keep to paths across farm land
- Avoid damaging fences, hedges and walls
- Leave no litter
- Safeguard water supplies
- Protect wildlife, wild plants and trees
- Go carefully along country roads
- Respect the life of the country side

Do please take reasonable precautions as at times the walks can be isolated.

Key

- ⊙ Circular walk
- 🚶 Buggyable
- 🚲 Suitable for bike rides
- * Walk off OS Map 1183

See Map on Pages 138/9

1. Beechwood

Map ref.: OS 759621
Directions by car and parking: From top of Ralph Allen Drive, down The Avenue, down Summer Lane to Beechwood Road. Park (usually easy). **By bus:** No.2 from Southgate to Combe Down
Length of walk: 1 hour. Hilly.
Obstacles: Steps and stile. Beware dog poo.
Points of interest: Pooh sticks, lovely views, stream. **Surface:** Grass, can be muddy.
Picnic spot: OS 759616. Turn right at stream.
Refreshments: The Rockery, Combe Down (see **Eating Out**).
Route: signposted over grass, follow signs down to stream. Steep decline, narrow path
Comments: Could become a little overgrown. Best in Spring or Autumn.

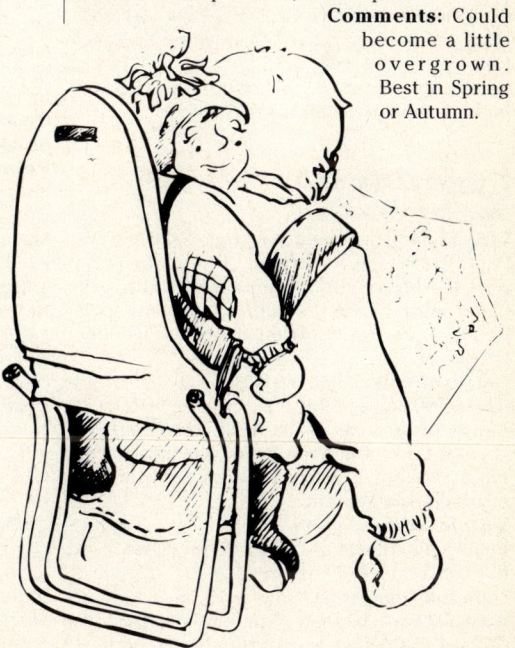

Walks

2. Breach Wood, Englishcombe ⓞ
Map ref: OS 728629
Directions by car and parking: Take A367 from Bath. At the roundabout with "The Red Lion" pub on corner turn right along Rush Hill. Park in Culverhay School Visitors overflow car park up the hill from the school. Parking easy.
By bus: No 720. Get off at Culverhay School.
Length of walk: 1 hour 20 minutes. Hilly.
Obstacles: Stile, fence to climb.
Points of interest: kite-flying, boats, blackberrying, good views, lots of horses, goats, ducks and dogs.
Surface: Grass and mud - can be muddy.
Picnic spot: Just before or after the wood, or Twerton Round Hill or Rush Hill on the way home - a diversion with brilliant views.
Refreshments: Newsagent on Rush Hill, few yards from car park. Whiteway Garden Centre.
Route: Follow path on left of school for 200 yards, climb over stile on right hand side into field. The bottom of the field turns into a muddy stream. Climb over fence and continue up hill and into Breachwood through stile. Walk through wood - this emerges onto a field, ploughed in winter, and continue to Englishcombe Village. Take first right past red brick terrace and up rough track on to Rush Hill. Turn right for car park.
Comments: Backpack only. Can be overgrown in parts. Best in the Spring or Summer.

3. Brown's Folly ⓞ
Map ref: OS 786669
Directions by car and parking: Take the A4 from Bath to Bathford. Once through Batheaston, at roundabout take right fork under bridge. Take first left. "The Crown" pub is on the corner. Park on the road (usually easy).
Length of walk: 2 hours. Hilly.
Obstacles: Steps, stile.
Points of interest: Spectacular views across Limpley Stoke and Avon Valley, blackberrying, cows, sheep, chickens, farm equipment, disused quarry entrances.
Surface: Mud and grass.
Picnic spot: Bench near folly - good views.
Refreshments and toilets: "The Crown" pub - good food (see **Pubs**).
Route: From "The Crown" pub walk up the hill. Go past Post Office and turn right and up into Dovers Lane. Continue until the folly is signposted. Go over stile and up the hill, head towards the houses (can be muddy). At the top of the field exit over stile and onto the road. Follow signpost on your right up narrow track. This meets a gravel path obliquely. Take path in same direction. In approx. 100 yards turn right at fork. In approx. 700 yards take the steep path signposted on your left. At white-topped post, sidestep left and continue up for 50 yards. Take steps up on your left. Turn right at top of steps about 20 yards from dry stone wall. Could take another path down, back through village, past church and back
Comments: Walk involves crossing some roads at the beginning, all quiet except for the main road near "The Crown". Backpack only. Entrances to stone mines - adult supervision needed. Do watch for steep drops from paths in places. A variety of walks to the folly, this is just one of them. Map useful.

4. Engine Wood, near Combe Hay ⓞ
Map ref: OS 746604
Directions by car and parking: From Bath take B3110 toward Hinton Charterhouse. At Midford turn right towards Combe Hay, follow lane for approx half a mile. Stop and park in layby on right, 1 - 2 cars only.
Length of walk: 1 hour. Hilly.
Obstacles: Steps, stile and stream to cross - no bridge.
Points of interest: Views, blackberrying, horses, abandoned Somerset coal canal, beech wood, disused railway line, stream.
Surface: Grass, earth, stone and mud.
Picnic spot: In meadows near stream or hillside between stream and Southstoke.
Refreshments: "Packhorse Inn", Southstoke. See **Pubs**.
Route: Walk under railway arch by Somerset Coal Canal information board and over stile. Disused locks on left hand side. Turn left at gate, cross sleeper bridge over steam, up the hill through Engine Wood, steps roughly cut into hillside. At top, knee high arch, old canal on right. Straight on over stile and turn right up hill away from canal. At top of field bear right across field, cross stile in hedge and down very steep field - wood on right. Follow path across stream. Turn right to return to car. Or turn left and up the hill across fields to Southstoke and the "Packhorse Inn" See **Pubs**.

128 Bath with your Kids

Walks

Comments: Exciting scramble for toddlers, good backpack walk, lovely wood. Canal used to transport coal from the Somerset coal field to Bath. Site of a "caisson" lock.

5. Freshford to Avoncliff * ◯

Directions by car and parking: As Freshford Lanes (walk no.20).
Length of walk: 1 hour.
Obstacles: Stile, gate.
Points of interest: Aquaduct, trains, blackberrying, narrow boats and cruisers.
Surface: Mud and grass.
Picnic spot: In field near "The Inn" pub or at Avoncliff.
Refreshments and toilets: Cafe at Avoncliff next to footpath. Garden with rabbits. Home made cakes. "Cross Guns" Avoncliff - food and garden, see **Pubs**. "The Inn" at Freshford - good pub food and garden, see **Pubs**.
Route: From "The Inn" go over bridge and turn left through gate. Follow path through field and long river to Avoncliff. Can walk back to Freshford along towpath or catch train back to Freshford or Bath.
Comments: Can be busy in the summer, especially Sundays. Could continue to Bradford-on-Avon. Route can be overgrown and a bit dog messy. Backpack only.

6. Freshford Woods * ◯

Directions by car and parking: As Freshford Lanes (walk no.20).
Directions by train: As Freshford Lanes.
Length of walk: 1 hour. Hilly.
Obstacles: Stiles.
Points of interest: Pooh sticks, river, sheep, chickens.
Surface: Mud and grassy fields.
Picnic spot: In the last field before returning to "The Inn" pub.
Refreshments and toilets: "The Inn" pub.
Route: Take footpath through swing gate to the left of "The Inn" pub into the field. The path is narrow, steep and often muddy. Walk through the swing gate at the top and turn left. Proceed down the path and through the woods and into the fields at the bottom. Follow the river and go across the stile. At the road turn left over the bridge. Follow road round to the stile on the left. Cross the field back to the road and turn left, which brings you back to the pub
Comments: Walk involves crossing quiet village lanes. Backpack only. Could make good combination with a train journey - directions as Freshford Lanes .

7. Lansdown Race Course and Prospect Stile

Map Ref: OS 726686
Directions by car and parking: Drive up Lansdown Road and park on slip road opposite "Blathwayt Arms" pub. Parking easy.
Length of walk: 1 hour. Hilly.
Obstacles: Stile.
Points of interest: Good kite-flying, blackberrying, spectacular views, cows and wildlife.
Surface: Grass and mud - can get quite muddy.
Picnic spot: Prospect Stile - a bench with magnificent views to the Mendips and Bristol - you can see Clifton Suspension Bridge.
Refreshments and toilet: "Blathwayt Arms" - see **Pubs**.
Route: Start at corner of pub's car park and follow path leading towards the perimeter rail of the race course. Cross the course and then follow the wall to your left, beyond which the ground falls away to the South. After about a mile along the grassy track you come to Prospect Stile with a bench and magnificent views to the Mendips and Bristol. Return the way you came.
Comments: Not suitable on race days or for very young children. From Prospect Stile you could continue on a number of superb walks taking you to Kelston hill or the isolated village of North Stoke. For these you would need a map and it can be muddy. Best to do walk on clear days when view from Prospect Stile is breathtaking and Clifton Suspension Bridge can be seen. Beware of dog poo.

8. Little Solsbury Hill ◯

Map ref: OS 770678
Directions by car and parking: Take A4 from Bath towards Batheaston. At Batheaston turn left, signposted Northend and St. Catherines. After 150m turn left up Solsbury Lane. After quarter mile at fork bear right, go along Little Solsbury Lane (No through road) and park. Parking for limited number of cars.
Length of walk: Various walks 1 hour, depending on route. Hilly.

Bath with your Kids 129

Walks

Obstacles: Stiles, possibly a fence to climb.
Points of interest: Site of Iron Age fort. Flat-topped hill with panoramic views of Bath. Good kite-flying. Cows.
Surface: Grass - can be muddy in wet weather
Picnic spot: On top of hill - no benches.
Route: Go through gate, walk up hill. Can go on a variety of circular walks from here.
Comments: Spectacular panoramic views. Refreshingly blowy. Excellent for kite flying but can be very cold, wrap up warm. Some lovely circular walks from Bailbrook Lane and Northend - look at O S map. Pushchairs only for those with great determination.

9. Perrymead

Map ref: OS 762627
Directions by car and parking: Park in The Avenue, Combe Down and walk back to the cross roads - Ralph Allen Drive, North Road and The Avenue. "The Hadley" pub is on one corner. Parking usually easy.
By bus: No 2 from Southgate.
Length of walk: 1 hour.
Points of interest: Stone arch, cows, sheep. Spectacular and interesting views down into Lyncombe Vale and Perrymead across to Widcombe Hill.
Surface: Tarmacadam, gravel and mud in equal proportions.
Refreshments: "The Rockery", North Road, Combe Down. See *Eating Out*.
Toilets: Near "Rockery" - public loos on North Road.
Route: From "The Hadley" pub cross North Road and take the footpath called Pope's Walk, behind the houses and Ralph Allen Drive. Follow path along the edge of Fox Hill estate and M.O.D. land. Go under stone arch and into pretty steep lane which becomes a road - cemetery to right. At T-junction with Perrymead turn right. This brings you to the bottom of Ralph Allen Drive. Take No 2 bus back to The Avenue or walk - long and steep hill. Buses every 10 minutes weekdays, few on Sundays.
Comments: Best in dry weather. Path between the arch and Perrymead runs with water and is slippery and muddy in wet weather. Can be a little dog messy near Fox Hill estate. Backpack only.

10. Smallcombe Vale

Map ref: OS 760644
Directions by car and parking: From Pulteney Road turn into Pulteney Gardens. Go over canal then bear left into Horseshoe Walk. Park on the road - usually easy. Walk starts at pot-holed track leading to cemetery on the right.
Length of walk: 2 hours. Hilly. A variety of circular routes.
Obstacles: Gate.
Points of interest: Interesting views of Bath., cows and blackberrying.
Surface: Grass.
Refreshments: City centre or shops on Bathwick Hill.
Toilets: Corner Pulteney Road and North Parade.
Route: Follow track which leads to cemetery. Can then make circular walk by either following diagonal path across the field to the south of the cemetery, then double back on opposite diagonal across the next field to Widcombe Hill.
Or: Pass round the back of Smallcombe Farm which eventually brings you out on Bathwick Hill.
Comments: Best in the Spring for the bluebells. Track is buggyable. The two paths which terminate on Bathwick Hill or Widcombe are fairly muddy and unsuitable for buggies.

11. Southstoke

Map ref: OS 748613
Directions by car and parking: Leave Bath on the 3110 towards Midford. At "The Cross Keys" pub, take road to Southstoke. As you come into the village there is a grass triangle, keep right and park round triangle - usually easy.
Length of walk: 1 hour. Hilly.
Obstacles: Stile.
Points of interest: Tunnel, spectacular views, wildlife, blackberrying, disused canal.
Surface: Gravel and mud.
Picnic spot: Approximately 50 yards from start of walk, there is a bench with views over the valley.
Refreshments and toilets: "Packhorse" pub in centre of Southstoke - see *Pubs*.
Route: Follow road straight on past electricity substation to fork (approx. 50 yards). Follow signpost on right of bench, through gateway.

Follow path across the field and down into the valley. Follow path along stream and parallel with disused canal. You eventually reach a train tunnel next to Combe Hay Lane. On the tunnel is a notice giving history of the Canal. WARNING: Take care near canal as it has steep sides and loose stones.
Comments: Backpack only. On clear day can see Westbury White Horse

12. Stoney Littleton, Longbarrow Wellow *
Map Ref: OS 732572
Directions by car and parking: Take A367 from Bath. At "Lamplighter" pub turn left, signposted Wellow. Follow lane for approx. 2 miles. At T-junction in village, turn right and drive to edge of village. After last farm on left hand side turn left, signposted Longbarrow. Follow lane round for 1 mile and park on left opposite house. Grassy parking area.
Length of walk: 1 hour to Barrow. Hilly. 1-2 hours to Wellow. Hilly.
Obstacles: Stile.
Points of interest: Sheep and more sheep, pooh sticks, ducks, views to Wellow and factory farm, Neolithic Barrow, fast flowing stream, bridge.
Surface: Mud, grass.
Picnic spot: By stream near bridge.
Refreshments and toilets: "Fox and Badger" pub, Wellow see **Pubs**.
Route: To Barrow. Cross stream using bridge at back of car park and over stile. Turn left up path over trickle of a stream and up hill. Turn left into field at stile with signpost to Longbarrow. Cross field and over stile on your right. Cross short field and pass through iron gate. Proceed to Barrow. Return following the same route.
Or: Continue to Wellow. Retrace your steps to stile signposted Long Barrow and then continue up hill to road which takes you down hill. Keep turning left until you reach Wellow. Retrace your car journey back to the car park.
Comments: Quiet roads to cross if you do the circular walk into Wellow. Backpacks only. Can be extremely muddy in wet weather, so take wellies. Neolithic Barrow (2000 BC) reputed to be one of the best in Britain. Well signposted. Nice trot for a toddler. Take a torch to peer into barrow.

13. Tucking Mill
Map ref: OS 766616
Directions by car and parking: From Bath take B3110 towards Midford. Turn left, signposted Monkton Combe. After approx half a mile park on left near Tucking Mill. **Or:** From top of Ralph Allen Drive cross into The Avenue. Turn right at T-junction near school and turn first left down Summer Lane. After 1.5 miles turn right, signposted Midford/Tucking Mill. Park on right after Tucking Mill gate.
Length of walk: 2 hours. Hilly.
Obstacles: Steps, stiles, gate, cows in field, weir on river, steep river bank.
Points of interest: Midford Castle, deer, cows, blackberrying, pooh sticks, tunnel (can't go through), disused railway track (good for pretending to be trains), viaduct and reservoir at Tucking Mill.
Surface: Grass, gravel, mud and tarmacadam, equal proportions.
Picnic spot: Near river in summer only.
Refreshments and toilets: "Hope and Anchor" pub, Midford has a small terraced garden. "Wheelrights Arms" pub, Monkton Combe - good beer and nice garden.
Route: Follow footpath on left of Gothic cottage which comes out alongside reservoir before railway viaduct. Turn left up steep steps (wooden, in poor condition). Brings you out at start of disused railway line. Follow track until you reach blocked tunnel. On the hill on your right is Midford Castle, on the left are railway sidings. Look out for gate on left hand side and go through, turning right and scramble through to lane. If you want to see disused tunnel continue on path and backtrack to gate and follow as above. Follow lane to crossroads, turn left down hill to "Hope and Anchor" pub car park. Old station visible from car park. Turn right at pub, cross river on main road, take first left into lane. After approx. 200 yards take footpath on left (signposted) over stile and across fields, sometimes tame deer in field. After muddy, dingy bit alongside railway embankment, path runs alongside river in meadows. Cross stile and turn left over footbridge, follow path over sluice gates. Turn left near old mill and follow path up hill into Mill Lane and into Monkton Combe village. Old village lock-up on right. At T junction turn left, ("Wheelrights" pub on left) continue up lane into churchyard.

Bath with your Kids 131

Walks

Leave through kissing gate. Turn left into the lane which takes you back to the start.
Comments: Backpacks. Watch children near fast-running mill race. Can be overgrown, very pretty, lots to see.

14. Bannerdown

Map ref: OS 794688
Directions by car and parking: From Bath take A4 to Batheaston. Park in the car park opposite the "George and Dragon" pub and walk up Fosse Lane to right of the pub or drive up Bannerdown Hill until you reach a straight piece of road (The Fosse Way). Park in the layby on the left. Parking easy.
Length of walk: 1–2 hours depending on how far you want to walk. Hilly.
Obstacles: Bank at start of walk. Beware low-flying cyclists!
Points of interest: Kite-flying, blackberrying, wildlife, good views, cows. Brilliant for hide and seek with older children.
Surface: Mud and grass.
Picnic spot: At start of walk.
Toilets: Batheaston car park - but lots of bushes.
Route: From layby clamber over bank with pushchair/bicycle/tricycle. Start walking.
Comments: This is a quarried, wooded area over which children can run, climb, play hide and seek and various other games. The walk can be as long or short as you want. Pushchair only for those with determination if you walk up Fosse Lane and up path, but can carry pushchair over bank to common from layby.

15. Rainbow Wood

Map ref: OS 765628
Directions by car and parking: Park on Claverton Down Road opposite Shaft Road - usually easy - no roads to cross.
By bus: No 2 from Southgate to top of Ralph Allen Drive.
Length of walk: Walk 1: 20 minutes, Walk 2: 1 hour. Low hills, Walk 3: 2 hours + bus ride. Hilly
Obstacles: Kissing gate, steps and stiles.
Points of interest: Sculptures for children to explore, brass rubbing on notice board, views of city centre, blackberrying.
Surface: Mainly grass - can get long in summer, track which is prone to puddles.
Picnic spot: On your left in sheltered field/copse before you get to playing field.
Refreshments: "The Rockery", North Road see Eating Out.
Toilets: To right of Claverton Down Road when heading towards Ralph Allen Drive.
Route: Walk through gated entrance. On your left is the remains of a beech wood largely destroyed by storms in January 1990, and a noticeboard. On your right is a mature beech wood. Walk straight ahead and into the field with rugby pitches.
Walk 1: Walk round field and return to car.
Walk 2: Walk round field in an anticlockwise direction until you come to kissing gate. Go through gate, bear left and pass under young trees. Cross stile and go down flight of steps in wood. At bottom follow path (good views of city). *A* at next stile turn left up hill, go back into original field via stile or gate. Continue round field back to car.
Walk 3: As for Walk 2, until *A*. At stile, turn right and go over stile and down hill through fields to lake at bottom of Prior Park gardens. Follow lane to Widcombe Church and turn left for the bottom of Ralph Allen Drive or straight on for Widcombe Hill. Walk or take bus back up Ralph Allen Drive.
Comments: Buggy with determination, best in dry weather.

16. Canal/River/Meadows

Map ref: OS 781674
Directions by car and parking: Park in free car park at Batheaston opposite "George and Dragon".
By bus: No 13, 13a, 231 from Bus station to Stambridge, Batheaston.
Length of walk: 1.5-2 hours.
Obstacles: Tree roots on river walk, steps and stiles, OK with buggy in dry weather but need to lift buggy over stiles and down steps, with determination when muddy.
Points of interest: Blackberrying, feeding ducks, trains, rowing boats, barges, water wheel, weir, sheep and cows, goats and geese, boating at Avondale hotel.
Surface: Mud, tarmac, grass.
Picnic spot: Best spots by canal near "The George", Bathampton or at "Secret Garden" by car park at the start.
Refreshments: "Old Mill", "Bathampton Mill",

Walks

"Avondale Hotel (Duck and Punt)" and "The George" see **Eating Out**.
Route: From car park follow path along river adjacent to Secret Garden, take care as there's a lot of tree roots and can be muddy. Excellent views across meadows, some good duck/swan feeding spots. Continue along river and look out for a field of goats on right hand side, also a garden full of geese. Proceed to end of path and bear right up to road past the "Old Mill" (see **Eating Out**), turn left, double back on road past "Old Mill" and its water wheel, over toll bridge, look out for ducks, past "Bathampton Mill - Beefeater"(see **Eating Out**) and continue along road for half a mile until "The George" (see **Eating Out**). Go past pub, through gate on right and turn left along canal. You can picnic here, then go under bridge, look out for narrow boats, until house on left hand side. Just before house, leave canal and turn down path to left to join lane. Turn right on to lane and continue until railway crossing, (read notice carefully, lots of Intercity trains) by stile and cross another stile on other side (there are gates if you have a pushchair) and go down steps to field. Cross meadow, normally full of cows, and over a stile, cross diagonally left over another meadow and look for stile and go up path. Can be overgrown in Summer, but is wonderful for blackberries, climb embankment, cross river by railway bridge (trainspotting) and come to railway line on left, descend embankment and come out on main road, turn left under bridge and go straight on, crossing busy roundabout by pedestrian crossing. Avondale Hotel and Duck and Punt on left are good for cream teas and boating, and continue along road for half a mile to start. Secret garden lovely for a run around, picnic, apples, blackberries and good view of river and some nice statues.
Comments: Meadows and river path flood in very heavy rain, can be muddy, wear wellies and forget the pushchair unless you don't mind very muddy wheels. Lots of rural views and ducks. Beautiful walk.

17. Canal

Map ref: OS 759655
Directions by car and parking: Take A36 from Bath. Shortly after the Bathwick roundabout you pass over the railway and then over the canal. Park near canal bridge.

Length of walk: 2 hours.
Obstacles: Stiles.
Points of interest: Boats, tunnels, trains, black-berrying, wildlife, sheep and horses.
Surface: Grass and gravel.
Picnic spot: Along canal on benches.
Refreshments and toilets: "The George" (see **Pubs**).
Route: Head eastwards (away from the city) along the towpath. The buildings give way to open countryside. After 1.5 miles of easy walking you reach "The George" pub. You could go back the way you came or, to make a circular walk, take the road northwards from "The George" and cross the railway bridge. Soon you will see opening in the hedge on your left. Go through. This route leads back along the river meadows to rejoin the canal and the start point. Follow footpath signs carefully, footpath crosses by-pass. Backpacks only as there are stiles and a kissing gate to negotiate.
Comments: Opportunities for feeding ducks and picnics beside canal. Very popular walk, can be busy on good days. One busy road to cross.

18. Canal and River

Map ref: OS 755642
Directions by car and parking: Park in Widcombe, near the shops or in the car park. Usually easy - but check time limit on street.
Length of walk: 1 hour.
Obstacles: Steps, ramp.
Points of interest: Locks, canal, ducks, swans, trains, narrow boats, tunnel, parks, blackberrying, wildlife if vigilant. Beazer maze see **Parks**.
Surface: mostly tarmac, some puddles, chippings and mud.
Picnic spot: Sydney Gardens, Henrietta Gardens or benches along the river. Parade Gardens.
Refreshments: Bathwick Hill Post Office and General Store, City centre facilities. Museum of Holbourne Tea House - see **Eating Out**.
Toilets: Sydney Gardens, Henrietta Gardens, Widcombe.
Route: Start walk at canal in Widcombe. Follow towpath to Sydney Gardens, approx 1 mile. Go up step and through ornamental iron gate. Cross Sydney Gardens. Cross Sydney Place - busy road - down Sutton Street and into Henrietta Park. Cross park towards Laura

Bath with your Kids 133

Walks

Place. Proceed towards City centre along Argyle Street. At Grove Street, turn right then first left. This will take you down to the river and avoids a flight of stairs. You will pass under Argyle Street and emerge with the garden of "The Boater" pub on your left, shortly followed by Beazer Maze. Carry on with the river on your right towards Thimble Mill and Widcombe.
Comments: Lots to see and do en route. Pleasant and varied urban walk. Can be done with buggy, bicycle or tricycle. Towpath can get a little overgrown and puddly in places. It can also be a bit dog messy. Keep off the verges! Lots of cyclists in summer.

19. Claverton Down Woods
Map ref. OS 772628
Directions by car and parking: Up Ralph Allen Drive and turn left at top. Park on road (2 spaces) or just after Bath Clinic opposite Ralph Allen School (limited).
Length of walk: 1 hour.
Obstacles: Stiles, gate.
Points of interest: Beech trees, scrunchy leaves. **Surface:** Grass - can be long in summer - generally dry.
Picnic spot: In meadow - some lovely spots, but noisy traffic on main road.
Route: Go through narrow gated entrance (OK for buggy) with National Trust signpost.
Route A: Go through the stile and gate (opens for a buggy) then right and follow path through wood. At end of wood either turn right and over stile back through field and back to start near road. Beware of dog poo.
Route B: Turn left past back of large house over stile and through more woods, through kissing gate (gate for buggies) and into meadow. Turn right for main road over another stile. Once on road turn right and return to car park.
Route C: Turn left and follow path across fields then back the way you came.
Comments: Buggyable with lifting over stiles.

20. Freshford Lanes *
Directions by car and parking: Leave Bath on A36. After approx 6 miles turn left, signposted to Freshford. The road drops down into the centre of Freshford and continues down another steep hill until you reach "The Inn" pub on your right. Park in the pub car park - easy depending on time of day.
Length of walk: 2 hours.
Points of interest: 2 bridges - pooh sticks, birds, sheep, chickens, spectacular views.
Surface: Tarmacadam.
Picnic spot: In field near pub or on the Tyning between Sharpstone and the village centre.
Refreshments and toilets: "The Inn" pub and garden - see **Pubs**.
Route: Turn right out of the pub car park, take right turns at each road junction. Half way up steep hill turn right into Sharpstone Lane - has some charming stone cottages and views to Iford. At the end of Sharpstone the lane goes across The Tyning - an open piece of land on a straight ridge. The last leg of the walk is through the centre of Freshford. Turn right again down the hill and back to the pub.
Comments: Good combination with a train. Leave Freshford station. Walk along Station Lane, turn left at end and walk down the hill until you reach "The Inn" pub on your right 5-10 minutes. Good circular walk with one steep hill to climb. All accessible by pushchair. Walk involves crossing quiet village lanes. Care needed in places as there can be dog mess.

21. Linear Park (Bear Flat to Sandpits)
Map ref: OS 745636
Parking: Maple Grove or Bloomfield Road - easy.
By bus: No 3 from Southgate to Bear Flat. Get off opposite "Bear" pub. Walk up Wellsway and along Bloomfield Road. Start of walk - recreation field on your right
Length of walk: Half hour to Sandpits play area, or can make it longer by continuing along the Linear Park to the Lower Bristol Road.
Points of interest: Birds, squirrels, plants, berries. **Surface:** Gravel.
Toilets: Junction of Wellsway and Bloomfield Road, Sandpits play area.
Route: From Bear Flat take right fork up Bloomfield Road. At recreation ground on right leave road and cross field past nice play area and cross field, exit bottom left. Follow disused railway to Sandpits play area. Return the way you came.
Or: Continue along Linear Park and out onto the Lower Bristol Road.
Comments: Beware dog mess. Walk does involve crossing roads, not too busy. Pleasant "green" route through residential area.

134 Bath with your Kids

Walks

22. Lyncombe Vale

Map ref: OS 751635
Directions by car and parking: From Bear Flat take left fork after Devonshire Road and second left down Greenway Lane. Take first right down Lyncombe Vale Road and park on road after The Paragon School. Parking easy.
Length of walk: 1.5 hours. Hilly.
Obstacles: Stile and possibly steep flight of steps depending on route.
Points of interest: Stream, with frogs and tadpoles, squirrels, birds, butterflies, flowers, wild strawberries in June, blackberries in Autumn.
Surface: Grass, gravel and mud - can get quite muddy in places.
Picnic spot: In field at start of walk and at entrance to tunnel.
Route: Cross wooden stile on your left, see stream, walk ahead and double back onto higher level and disused railway. You can then go left or right. Right leads to a blocked tunnel - pretty views. Come back the same way. Left takes you on a circular walk. Follow path to tunnel. Either follow footpath on your right which takes you up a very steep flight of steps and onto the Entry Hill end of Greenway Lane which we will call point *A*
Or: Follow path to the left which leads along a sheltered path between the hedges known as "muddy bottoms walk". This emerges on Inbrook. Follow road up the hill to the right which meets Entry Hill. Go down Entry Hill and turn right again at Greenway Lane. Note steep flight of steps on your right between houses; this is the alternative route up from railway footpath. *A* Follow Greenway Lane, turn right down Lyncombe Vale Road past The Paragon School and back to the start.
Comments: A refreshing, pretty walk with lots to see. Hilly.

23. Sham Castle

Map ref: OS 768646
Directions by car and parking: Up North Road and take the Quarry Road access to the University on your left. Park ing usually easy.
By Bus: No 18, 19, 721.
Length of walk: 2 hours. Hill.
Obstacles: Steps, stiles, route can become partly overgrown.
Points of interest: Folly, kite-flying, blackberrying, wildlife, cows, views to Bathampton and Avon Valley.
Surface: Tarmacadam and mud - best in dry conditions.
Picnic spot: Sham Castle - no seats.
Route: Walk to the left of the footbridge which you passed under. Sham Castle is a few hundred yards away. Beyond the castle you can walk through the Golf Club onto the Down, which is cattle-grazing land. You will need the 1:2500 map to complete the delightful 2 mile circular walk around the Down with its views to Bathampton and the Avon Valley and back to Sham Castle.
Comments: A choice of delightful circular walks. We recommend that you take a 1:2500 map. Sham Castle is a Georgian folly which stands on Bathampton Down overlooking the city and is illuminated at night.

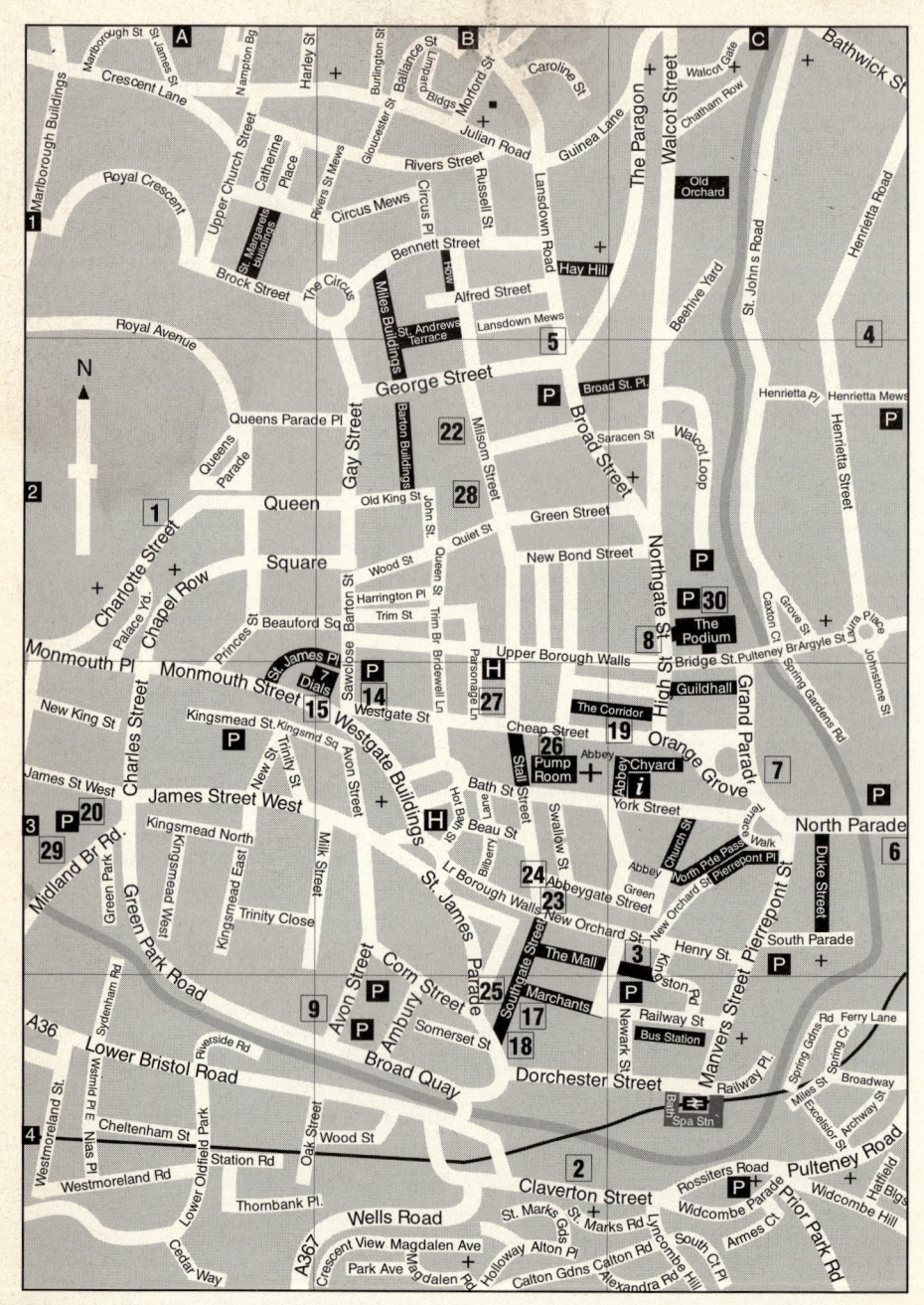

© Dentons Directory Ltd. The publishers gratefully acknowledge the support of Dentons Directories in allowing the reproduction of this map.

Location of Loos in City Centre

1. Charlotte Street Car Park
2. Claverton Street
3. Ham Gardens
4. Henrietta Park
5. Lansdown Road
6. North Parade Road
7. Parade Gardens
8. The Podium Shopping Centre
9. Riverside Coach Park
14. Sawclose
15. Seven Dials
17. Adams
18. Boots
19. Early Learning Centre
20. Green Park Station
22. Jolly's
23. Littlewoods
24. Marks and Spencer
25. Mothercare
26. Pump Room
27. WH Smith
28. Waterstones
29. Sainsburys
30. Waitrose

Park and Ride

There are four Park and Ride sites on the outskirts of Bath, each offering free parking with express Badgerline Bus services direct to the city centre, every 10-15 minutes.

Newbridge (A4)

Service 21
Monday-Saturday, 7.30am-7.30pm.
Setting down and picking up point at Westgate Buildings.

Lansdown

Service 31
Monday-Friday, 7.30am-7.30pm.
Setting down and picking up point at corner of Queen Square.

Odd Down

Service 41
Monday-Friday, 7.30am-7.30pm.
Setting down and picking up point at St. James' Parade.

Bath University, Claverton Down

Service 19
Saturdays only, 8.30am-6.30pm.
Setting down and picking up point at Terrace Walk.

A46
Lansdown Road
London Road
Julian Road
A4
A36
Upper Bristol Road
CITY CENTRE
Pulteney Road
Bathwick Hill
Ralph Allen Drive
Englishcombe Lane
Rush Hill
Wellsway
Entry Hill
© Bath With Your Kids

Walks Within City Boundary

1. Beechwood
2. Breach Wood, Englishcombe
7. Lansdown Race Course and Prospect Stile
8. Little Solsbury Hill
9. Perrymead
10. Smallcombe Vale
11. Southstoke
13. Tucking Mill
14. Bannerdown
15. Rainbow Wood
16. Canal/River/Meadows
17. Canal
18. Canal and River
19. Claverton Down Woods
21. Linear Park (Bear Flat to Sandpits)
22. Lyncombe Vale
23. Sham Castle

Parks and Play Areas within City Boundary

1. Alexandra Park
2. Alice Park
3. Ballance Street
5. Beacon Hill
6. Beazer Maze
7. Bloomfield Road
8. Brassmill Lane Open Space
9. Brickfield
10. Calton Road
11. Chandler Close
12. Corston View
13. Cranmore Place
14. Dartmouth Avenue
15. Dorset Close
16. Dunstar House
17. Firsfield
18. Excelsior Street
19. Green Park
20. Hedgemead Park
21. Henrietta Park
22. Homemead Park
23. Innox Park
24. Kelston Field
25. Kingsway
26. Larkhall Recreation
27. Loxton Drive
28. Midsummer Buildings
29. Moorlands Recreation Ground
30. Moorlands Sandpits
31. Mount Road
32. Newbridge Open Space
33. Parade Gardens
34. Parry Close
35. Pennyquick Open Space
36. Rosewarn Close
37. Roundhill Park
38. Royal Victoria Park
39. Snow Hill
40. Springfield Farm
41. St Saviour's Open Space
42. Sydney Gardens
43. Valley View Close
44. Weston Recreation Ground
45. Widcombe Open Space
46. Woodhouse Park

Bath with your Kids 139

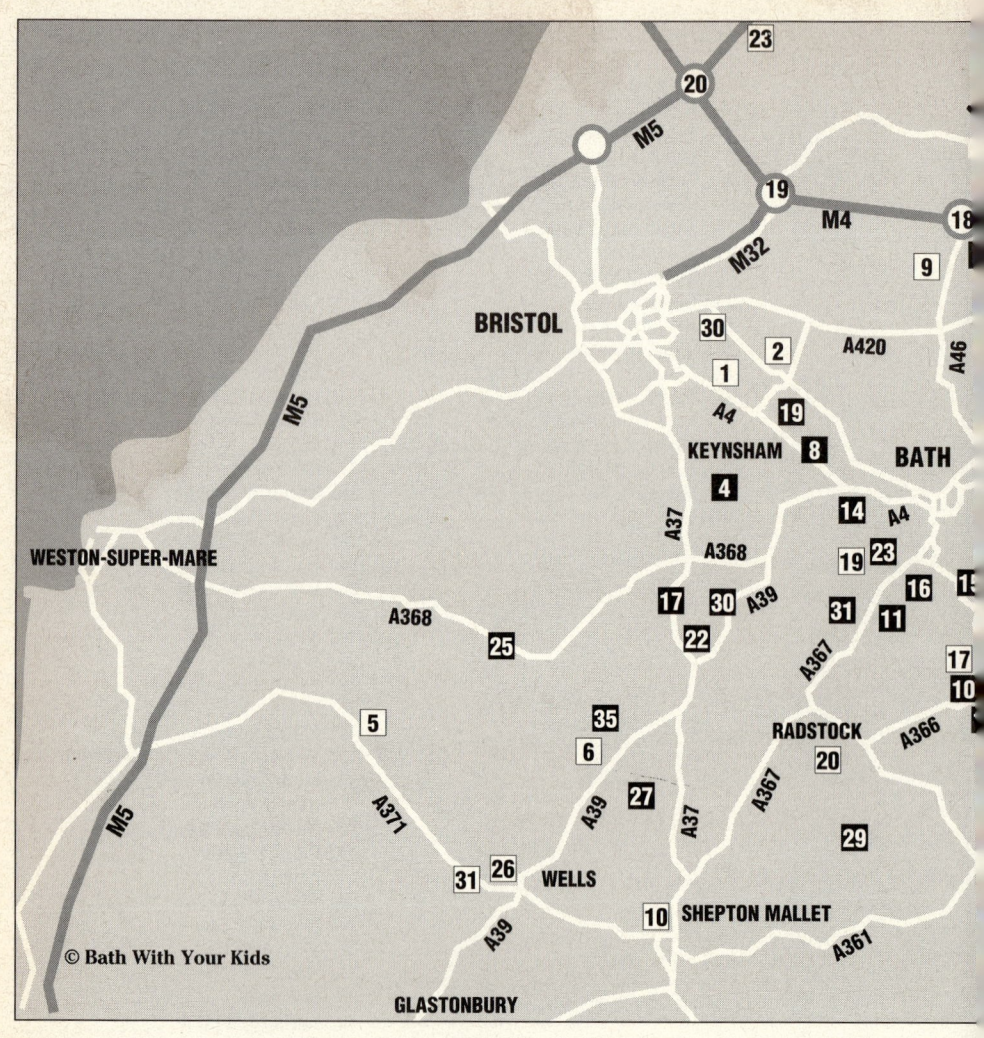

TRIPS AND JAUNTS OUTSIDE BATH

1. Avon Valley Country Park
2. Avon Valley Railway
3. Bowood House
4. Brokerswood and Woodland Heritage Museum
5. Cheddar Showcaves and Cheddar Gorge
6. Chewton Cheese Dairy
7. Corsham Court
8. Corsham Underground Quarry
9. Dyrham Park
10. East Somerset Railway
11. Farleigh Hungerford Castle
12. Iford Manor Gardens
13. Lackham Gardens and Museum
14. Lacock Village
15. Longleat House and Gardens
16. Longleat Safari Park
17. Norwood Farm
18. Pigs Folly

140 Bath with your Kids

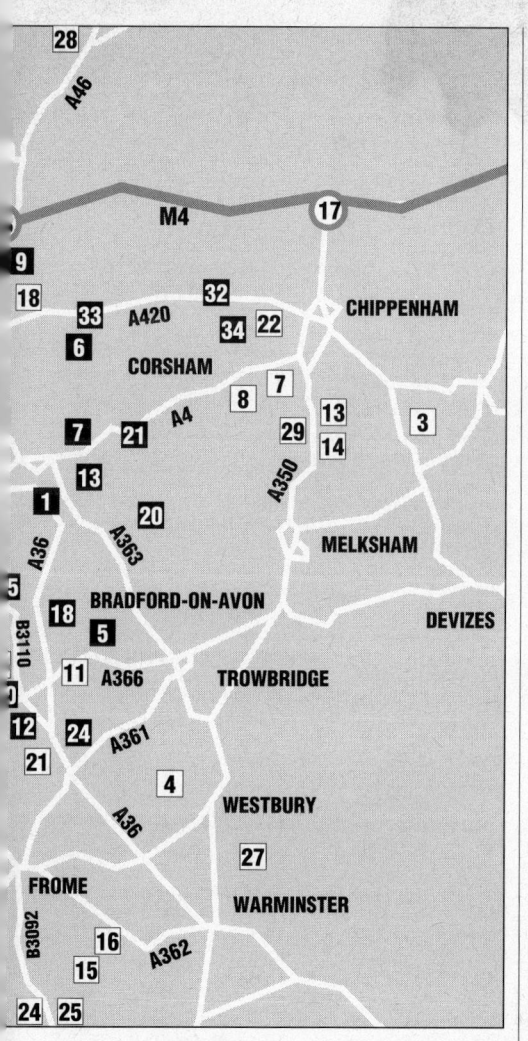

28. Westonbirt Arboretum
29. Whitehall Garden Centre
30. Willsbridge Mill Wildlife Trust
31. Wookey Hole Caves

PUBS OUTSIDE BATH

1. Bathampton Mill
2. Barge Inn, Bradford-on-Avon
3. Canal Tavern, Bradford-on-Avon
4. The Compton
5. Cross Guns
6. The Crown, Marshfield
7. The Crown, Bathford
8. The Crown, Saltford
9. The Crown Inn
10. Fleur de Lys
11. Fox and Badger
12. The George Inn, Norton St Philip
13. The George Inn, Bathampton
14. The Globe
15. Hop Pole
16. Hope and Anchor
17. Hunters Rest
18. The Inn at Freshford
19. Jolly Sailor
20. Longs Arms
21. Northey Arms
22. Old Station Inn
23. Packhorse Inn
24. Red Lion
25. Ring O'Bells
26. Riverside Bar, Bradford-on-Avon
27. Slabhouse Inn
28. The Swan Hotel, Bradford-on-Avon
29. Vobster Inn
30. Warwick Arms
31. Wheatsheaf
32. The White Hart, Ford
33. The White Hart, Marshfield
34. White Horse
35. Ye Olde Kings Arms

19. Priston Mill
20. Radstock, Midsomer Norton and District Museum
21. Rode Tropical Bird Gardens
22. Sheldon Manor
23. Slimbridge Wildfowl and Wetlands Centre
24. Stourhead House and Garden
25. Stourhead Alfred's Tower
26. Wells Cathedral and Close
27. Westbury White Horse

Bath with your Kids 141

Index

Abacus Day Nursery	45	Bath Chronicle	126	Bristol Hippodrome	58	Clay	17
ABC Inflatables	57	Bath Citizens Advice Bureau	7	Bristol Old Vic	58	Clifton Suspension Bridge	
Acknowledgments	2	Bath City Farm	61	Bristol Tourist Information	123	and Observatory	124
Acupuncture	66,67	Bath College of Higher		Bristol Zoo	30, 124	Combe Grove Manor Hotel	
Adams	100	Education Day Nursery	46	Brokerswood and Woodland		and Country Club	53, 97
Adoption	8,10	Bath and Dundas Canal		Heritage Museum	23, 54, 118	Combe Park Pre-school	51
Adult Education	98	Company	117	Brownies	24	Community Bus	70
Adult Sanctuaries	97	Bath Environment		Bryan the Magician	56	Computers	22
Advisory Centre for		Centre	61, 62	Building of Bath Museum	114	Contents	5
Education	8	Bath Festival	27	Burger King	38	Cookie the Clown	56
Adventure Playgrounds	112	Bath Fringe Festival	27	Buses	8,116	Cornerstone Coffee Shop	43
After School Clubs	9,22	Bath Industrial Heritage				Corsham Court	119
Alcohol	16	Centre	113	Cafes	37	Corsham Underground	
Alexander Technique	66	Bath Museum	114	Caffe Piazza	38,53	Quarry	119
Alexandra Park	82	Bath Organic Group	62	Cakes	103	Cot Death	16
Alice Park	82	Bath Postal Museum	113	California Kitchen	39	Cotswold Water Park	125
Cafe	53	Bath Puppet Theatre	53, 56	Canal Walks	132, 133	Country Dancing	17
American Museum	113	Bath Spa Hotel	37	Canalside Cafe	43	Craft Technique	102
Cafe	43	Bath Sports and Leisure		Canary, the	39	Cranial Osteopathy	67
Annual Events	27	Centre	53, 97, 109, 110	Cannon Cinema	58	Creative Activities	17
Anti-Bullying Campaign	8	Bath Unity Players	57	Canoeing	19	Cricket	19
Antenatal Care	64	Bath University	98	Car Safety	95	Cruse	16
Antenatal/Parentcraft		Bathampton Playgroup	50	Carwardine's Coffee		CRY-SIS	9
Classes	64	Bathford Pre-school	50	House	39	Cub Scout Groups	24
Aromatherapy	66	Bathtub Bistro	37	Castle Place Leisure		Culverhay Sports	
Art Clubs	17, 22	Baton Twirling	17	Centre	110	Centre	54, 109, 111
Athletics	19	Beaches	59	Caterpillars Day Nursery	46	Cycling Events	28
Atwell-Wilson Motor		Beavers	24	CD/CD Roms	77	Cycling Safety	95
Museum	125	Beazer Maze	82	Centre for Complementary			
Avon Fire Brigade	95	Beckford's Tower	114	Medicine	68	Dance	17
Avon Parents Network	7	Beechencliff Playgroup	50	Chaplin's Restaurant	39	Day Care Trust	9
Avon Valley Country		Before and After Club	34	Charlecombe Nursery, the		Day Nurseries	45
Park	117	Bella Pasta	37	Royal School	49	Demuths Vegetarian	
Avon Valley Cycles	104	Bereavement	16	Cheddar Gorge	118	Restaurant	39
Avon Valley Railway	117	Berkeley Castle	125	Cheddar Showcaves	118	Disability	15, 16
AvonSafe	95	Better Food Company	61	Chepstow Castle	125	Docks, Bristol	124
		Bikes	105	Chewton Cheese Dairy	118	Dolls Hospital	106
Baby and Toddler		Binks	37	Restaurant	43	Downs Syndrome	13
Groups	31	Birth Aids	74	Child Poverty Centre	9	Drama	18
Baby Equipment	99	Bitton Railway	30	Child Care	35	Drugs	16
Baby Sitters	36	Blaise Castle	123	Childline	9	Ducks, annual race	28
Badgerline Buses	8, 116	Bloomfield Nursery		Childminding	10, 35	Duck feeding spots	59, 112
Badminton	19	School	46	Children's Shoes/Clothes	76	Dyrham Park	119
Ballet	17, 18	Bloomsbury's	37	Chinese Medical Centre	68	Dyslexia	13
Balloon Events	27, 28, 81	Boathouse, the	43	Chippenham College	98	Dyspraxia	13
Band Concerts	28, 81	Boating Station	37, 116	Chiropractice	67		
Barnaby Pre-school	51	Boggle	5, 105	Christian Books	99	Early Learning Centre	106
Barnardo's Charity Shop	100	Bonfire Displays	29	Christie Miller Sports		East Somerset	
Baskervilles	19, 23, 53, 97	Bonghy Bo	38	Centre	110	Railway	30, 119
Basketball	19	Books	77, 99	Christmas Water Carnival	30	Eating Out	37
Bath Abbey Heritage		Boomerang	54, 57	Churches	87	Eczema	14
Vaults	113	Bouncers	57	Church Clubs	25	Education	45
Bath Area Play Group	25	Bouncy Castles	57	Cinemas	58	Adult	98
Bath Balloon Festival	27	Bowood House	118	City of Bath College	98	Appeal System	52
Bath Central Library	98	Boys Brigade	24	Day Nursery	47	Voucher Scheme	51
Bath Centre for Counselling		Bradford Pool	109	City Tours (buses)	116	Education Otherwise	52
and Psychotherapy	67	Breastfeeding	64, 65, 73	Clarendon Sports		Entertainment and	
Bath Centre for Voluntary		Bristol City Museum and		Centre	109, 111	Entertainers	53
Service	7, 98	Art Gallery	124	Claverton Pumping		Environment	61
Bath Childrens Festival	27	Bristol Docks	124	Station	114	Environmental Health	95

142 Bath with your Kids

Index

Epilepsy	14	Complementary	
Ethnic Support		Medicine	66
Organisations	11	Helicopter Museum	125
Evans Fish Restaurant	39,54	Henrietta Park	83
Exchange Trading System		Herbalism	67, 73
(LETS)	61	Hickory House	46
Exploratory Hands-on		Hillier Garden Centre Cafe	43
Science Centre	124	Hillside Playgroup	50
Explorers of the Lost		Hire Equipment -Bouncy	
World	54	Castles, Swing Boats,	
		Ball pools	57
Family Conciliation Service	8	Holbourne Museum	114
Farleigh Hungerford Castle	119	Tea House	40
Farms	62	Home Safety	96
Fathers	9	Homeopathy	67
Festivals	27	Hopscotch Nursery School	46
Fledglings Kindergarten	46	Housing, Bath And North	
Film Festival	29	East Somerset Housing	8
Firehouse Rotisserie	39	Bath Housing Advise Centre	8
Fireworks	29	Huxham Leisure	57
First Steps Nursery	47	Hyperactive	14
Fleet Air Museum	125		
Food Safety	96	Iford Manor Gardens	119
Football	19, 21	Il Bottelino	38
Footlights	39	Independent Schools	49
Fordside Tea Gardens	43	Industrial Museum	124
Fosseway Infant School	49	Instant Music	56
Fostering	8, 9, 10		
Free Events	29	Jabberwocky Montessori	
French	23, 79	Nursery School	47
Frome Community College	98	Jack and Jill Playgroup	50
Frome Leisure Centre	110, 111	Jack Stephens	56
Fun Fair	27	Jaunts	113
Fun, for free	29	Jazz Cafe	40
Funny Faces	56	Jeff Rodway	57
		John Dench	57
Garden Nursery, the	49	John Issacs and Mr Marvo	56
Garfunkels	39	John Rennie	54
Ghosts Walks	56, 116	Jolly's Department Store -	
Girls Brigade	24	Il Caffe and Terrace	
Glastonbury Childrens		Restaurant	40
Festival	28	Jolly Jumpers Amusement	
Global Action Plan	61	Hire	57
Green Issues	61	Judo	20
Green Park	83	Juggling	105
Green Park Brasserie	39		
Green Products	65	Kemble Nursery	48
Green Store, the	62, 75, 107	Kennet and Avon Canal	
Green Treats	68	Trust	117
Guide Friday	116	Keynsham Leisure Centre	110
Guided Walks	116	Kickers	97
Gymnastics	19	Kinder Garden, the	48
		Kingswood School	49
Haagen Daz	40	Kites	27, 29
Happy Days Nursery	46	Kite Flying Spots	59
Harvest	107		
Health Care	63	Lackham Gardens and	
In pregnancy	63	Museum	120
After Birth	64	Lacock Village	120
Children's	65	La Leche League	65

Language Clubs	22	Monkton Combe Junior	
Larkhall Playgroup Centre	50	School	49
Left-handed equipment	74	Montessori	22, 47, 48
Leisure Centres	20, 109, 110	Moorland Sandpits	84
LETS	61	Mosques	89
Libraries	69	Mrs Pickwick	55
Books	69	Mulberry House	22, 47
Central	69, 98	Multiple Births	9, 10
Mobile	69	Museums	113-126
STAR Multicultural	70	Museum of Costume and	
Summer Programme	25	Assembly Rooms	114
Toys	69	Museum of East Asian Art	114
WRVS	70	Music	
Literature Festival	27	Clubs	18, 26
Little Theatre	58	Musical Toddlers	33
Littlewoods Restaurant	40	Musicale Holidays	25
Loo Stops	71, 137	Shops	103
Longfellow Day Nursery			
(Norton Radstock		Nannies	35
College)	98	National Childbirth Trust	9, 65
Longleat House and		National Childminding	
Gardens	120	Association	10
Longleat Safari Park	121	National Playing Fields	
Lulsgate Airport	55	Association	81
		Natural Bedding/Fibres	75
Mail Order	73	Nature Clubs	23
Baby and Nursery		Nature Trails	112
Equipment	74	New Avenue Playgroup	50
Books	77	New Moon, the	40
CD Roms	77	NHS	63
Children's shoes/clothes	76	No. 5 Bistro	40
Green Products	75	Norton Radstock College	98
Outdoor Play	79	Norwood Farm	55, 62, 121
Party Items	80	Nursery Equipment	74
Pregnancy	73		
Stocking Fillers	80	Octagon Cafe, the	40
Toys and Gifts	78	Old Bell, the	43, 98
Maps	137	Old Mill Hotel, the	43
McDonalds	40, 54	Oldfield Park Playgroup	50
Magical Mandy	56	Old Orleans	41, 54
Magicians	56	Oliver Inn, the	41
Manvers Street Baptist		Olympiad	110, 111
Church	97	One Parent Families	10
Manvers Street Coffee Shop	40	Gingerbread	9
Markets	102	Open House Playgroup	50
Marmaris	40	Open Top Bus Tours	116
Marshfield Mummers	30	Open University	98
Martial Arts	20	Opportunity Playgroup	51
Maternity Alliance/Links	64	Organic Food Supplies	61
Maternity Clothes	73	Organic Gardening	62
Mencap	13	Osteopathy	67
Meningitis	14	Outdoor Play Equipment	79
Merlin Theatre and Arts			
Centre	58	Parade Gardens	85
Mews Nursery, the	48	Paragon School Nursery, the	49
Midsomer Norton Carnival	29	Pasta Galore	41
Miscarriage	16	Parent Associations	10
Model Centre	102	Parent and Toddler Groups	31
Monkeys Tweentown	55	Parentcraft Classes	64
Monks Coffee Shop	40	Parks and Play Areas	81, 139

Bath with your Kids 143

Index

Parks Department	81	Reflexology	67	Soft play	23	Nursery, the	48
Parkside Infant School	49	Relate	11	Special Needs	12	Tridias	106
Park Events	81	Regency Cafe	41	Splash Summer Play		Toys by Post	79
Parties	53	Regency Tours (buses)	116	Scheme	26	Trips	112, 141
Party Cakes	103	Reusable Nappies	62	Sports Activities	18	Twerton-on-Avon Infant	
Party Items	80, 103	Rickenbacker Food Co. 4	1	Sports Development	26	School	49
People and Planet	43	Riding	20	Spring Flower Show	27, 81	Twins	9, 10
Peppers	41	Riverford Farm	62	Springfield Leisure			
Peter Pan Playgroup	51	Road Safety	95	Centre	55, 110	Venue	126
Peter Stedman	56	Robin's Cinema	58	Springfield Playgroup	51	Victim Support	7
Pierre Victoire	41	Rockery, the	44	ss Great Britain	125	Victoria Art Gallery	115
Pigs Folly	55, 121	Rode Tropical Bird		ss Waverley and Balmoral	117	Victory Pre-school	48
Pinnocchio Day Nursery	47	Gardens	121	St Andrews CofE Primary		Vouchers, education,	
Pizza Express	41	Roller Skating	21	School	49	nursery	51
Pizza Hut	41	Roman Baths Museum	115	St Barnabas Players	58		
Places of Worship	87	Rondo	58	St John Ambulance	24	Walcot Cof E Infant School	49
Play Areas	81	Roy Grout	57	St Saviours CofE VC Infant		Walcot Montessori School	48
Play Groups	50	Royal Bath and West		School	49	Walks	116, 127, 139
Playbox Nursery	47	Show	28	Stables Restaurant	44	Walrus and the Carpenter	42
Police Community Affairs	95	Royal Crescent No 1	115	Stamp Shop	102	Wastenot Workshops	57
Pools	109	Royal Pavilion Cafe	42	STAR Multicultural Resource		Water Birth Services	74
Postnatal		Royal Photographic		Library	70	Waterstones	99
Illness	11	Society	115	State Schools, admission		Coffee Shop	42
Classes	65	Royal Victoria Park	85	policy	49	Wellow Trekking Centre	
Exercises	65, 97	Loos	71	Steiner		Parties	55
Pregnancy	63	Rugby	21	Toddler Group	34	Wells Cathedral and Close	122
Advisory Service	64			Fledglings Kindergarten	46	Westbury White Horse	123
Premature Clothes	75	Safety	95	Stepping Stones Playgroup	50	Westonbirt Arboretum	23, 123
Pre-school Learning		Sailing	21	Stillpoint	68	Weston Park Nursery	
Alliance	51	Sally Lunn's Museum	115	Stocking Fillers	80	School	48
Primary School Admission		Restaurant	42	Stourhead Alfred's Tower	122	Weston Playgroup	51
Policy	52	SANDS	16	Stourhead House and		Westwood Nursery	48
Prior Park Landscape		SATFA	16	Gardens	122	Widcombe Acorn Playgroup	50
Garden	115	Scoffs	42	Summer Clubs	26	Whitehall Garden Centre	123
Coffee Shop	43	Schools	49	Sunshine Playgroup	50	Wife of Bath	42
Priston Mill	121	Scrapstore	70	Swimming	21	Wildlife Trust	23
Public Houses	91	Seafoods	42	Swimming Pools and Sports		William Herschel	
Pubs	91, 141	Seymours Family Club	55	Centres	109	Museum	116
In Bath	91	Sheldon Manor	122	Sydney Gardens	86	Willsbridge Mill Wildlife	
Outside Bath	92	Shiatsu	67	Synagogues	89	Trust	123
Pulteney Bridge	117	Shoes	103			Windmill Hill City Farm	125
Pump Rooms, the	41	Shops	99	Tadpoles Nursery	47	Parties	55
Puppet Theatre	41	Baby Equipment	99	Tae Kwon-do	20	Windows Art Centre	
		Books	99	Tarte Flambee, La	42	Cafe	42
Race Issues	70	Charity Shops	100	Teasels Tearooms	44	Wookey Hole Caves	123
Radford Mill Farm	62	Clothes	100	Tennis	21	Woolley Grange Restaurant	
Radstock, Midsomer Norton		Maternity/Children	100	Textiles	17	and Hotel	44, 98
and District Museum	121	Hobbies	102	Theatre	18, 26, 57, 58	Woods	42
Rag Procession	29	Music	103	Theatre Royal	54, 58	Woodwork	17, 24, 98
Railways	29, 30, 117	Party Items	103	The Bath Month	126	Womens Associations	11
Rainbow Playgroup	51	Shoes	103	This Month in Bath	126	Women Returners	11
Rainbow Wood Farm	54	Sports/Bike and		Tilley's Bistro	42		
Rainy Days	112	Dancewear	104	Toddler Groups	31	Yate Leisure Centre	
Rascals Bistro	41	Toys	105	Toybox Toy Library	70	Parties	55
Real Meat Company	62	Simple Simon	57	Toys	78	YMCA	24
Real Nappy Company	62	Slimbridge Wildfowl and		Toy Shops	105	Y Tots Day Nursery	49, 97
Recreation Grounds	82	Wetlands Centre	122	Trading Standards	95	Youth Clubs	24
Recycling	62	Slings	74	Train Rides	112		
Red Cross	24	Smacking	9	Trampolining	21	Zilly the Clown	57
Red Lion Harvester	44	Social Services	8	Tree House Day		Zoo, Bristol	28, 30, 124

144 Bath with your Kids